Laboratory Manual
Introduction to Evolution and Evolutionary Genetics
Biology 152

Fourth Custom Edition for University of Toronto Mississauga
Edited by Professor Fiona Rawle, Nikki Sarkar, and Lisa Robertson

D1282066

Pearson Learning Solutions, 501 Boylston Street, Suite 900, Boston, MA 02116
A Pearson Education Company
www.pearsoned.com

Printed in Canada

1 2 3 4 5 6 7 8 9 10 XXXX 18 17 16 15 14

000200010271920567

JHA/IO

ISBN 10: 1-269-95702-3
ISBN 13: 978-1-269-95702-1

Table of Contents

Labs

Appendices

I. BIO152
Lab Policies

This section covers lab-related rules. You are responsible for reading, understanding and adhering to all course policies. Please read this section carefully. In addition, critical announcements may be made in lecture or in the LABS folder on the BIO152 Blackboard webpage.

1. **Labs start the first week of class** (see the course and lab schedule)

2. Labs start promptly at 2:10 pm, 3:40 pm and at 5:10 pm. Try to arrive early for every lab (i.e., at 2 pm, 3:30 pm or 5 pm). Marks may be deducted for lateness.

3. **Be prepared for your lab.** Read the entire lab, do the additional recommended readings, review the associated assignment or worksheet. Being well prepared will allow you to use your time in lab efficiently. Remember to bring your lab manual and associated worksheets to your lab period. *Note that lab coats ARE NOT REQUIRED but may be recommended for some labs.*

4. **Participate in lab.** Get to know the students that share your lab bench and be active during the lab by taking detailed notes, discussing lab concepts with your bench-mates, and asking questions.

5. **Finish on time.** The labs are designed to be completed on time. Students need to finish the lab, including the cleanup, by 5 minutes prior to the end of the lab session. Marks may be deducted for being late or leaving your work area messy.

6. **There are no make-up labs. If you miss a lab (for any reason), you cannot reschedule the lab for another time.** You are responsible for the lab material even if you miss that lab.

7. **Lab Worksheets and Assignments.** Labs 1, 3, 5, and 6 require the completion of in-lab worksheets due BEFORE you leave the lab. Labs 2, 4, and 7 require the completion of lab assignments that are due the following week (i.e., at the beginning of the next lab).

8. **Late Policy.** You must submit your in-lab worksheets and lab assignments on time. Late worksheets and assignments (regardless of the reason) will receive a mark of ZERO.

II. BIO152
Lab Safety

Before each lab: Read this information on Lab Safety and review what is pertinent to that lab exercise.

Safe Science in the lab

Emergency Response Guidelines
Telephones located in Prep Rooms DV1086 and DV1081

Local Telephone Numbers:
Campus Police   905-569-4333 DV3116
Peel Police   905-453-3311 or 9-911
Fire Department   9-911
Student Health Services   5255 (DV1123)
Credit Valley Hospital   905-820-6800
Ambulance   905-844-4242
Poison Information   1-800-268-9017
Environmental Protection Services 416-978-7000

General Rules

Please observe the following rules of conduct in the lab rooms.

1. **No food or drink (even water) is allowed in the lab**.
2. Wear appropriate clothing in the labs:
   - Wear a lab coat and disposable gloves if chemicals, microorganisms, or potential disease-causing organisms are handled (gloves are provided when required).
   - Do not wear open-toed shoes (or shorts or short skirts) in the lab.
3. Advise your TA and instructor of any special health conditions you have which they should know about in the event of an emergency.
4. Do not behave in any way that endangers the health and safety of other people in the class. Report any accidents, breakage, or damage of equipment immediately to your TA.
5. Clean up after yourself. Dispose of waste in the appropriate containers—broken glassware (and ONLY broken glassware) goes in the specially marked pail.
6. Wash your hands before leaving the lab.
7. **Do not wear disposable gloves outside the lab.**

Additional rules about handling chemicals, liquid solutions, and microorganisms

1. Always wear protective clothing.
2. Do not pipette solutions by mouth. Use the dispensers provided.

3. Keep solutions capped when not in use.

4. Dispose of solutions in the special labeled containers. Do not put solutions down the drain.

5. Read the safety data on the chemicals you will use so that you know what to do in case of a spill or emergency (see text below).

6. Wash your hands thoroughly before leaving the lab.

First Aid

For a minor injury
First aid kits, information guide, Emergency Response Guide, and Accident Report Forms are found in the Lab. All injuries, no matter what, should be reported to your TA.

For a serious injury or illness
Tell your TA or course technician immediately who will call the Campus Police at Local **4333** (a phone located in the prep room).

Chemical First Aid

Check the relevant material safety data sheets (MSDS) found in the Lab [by the door] for the recommended first aid procedure for each chemical you are using in a given lab. The three common chemical hazards are inhalation, ingestion, and skin/eye contact. For most chemicals the following basic first-aid procedures apply:

Inhalation: Move patient to fresh air.

Ingestion: Call poison control and notify (**1-800-268-9017**).

Skin/eye contact: Flush area with water for 15 minutes. Wash skin with soap and water. Consult physician if irritation persists. All labs are equipped with an eye-wash station.

Fire

1. Familiarize yourself with the location of fire exits and fire extinguishers at the beginning of your first lab, so you are prepared in case a fire breaks out in any of your labs.

In case a fire does happen:

2. **Tell your TA immediately.**

3. Attempt to extinguish a fire only if you can do so safely.

4. Each lab room has a fire extinguisher next to the door.

5. **Your TA or course technician** will activate the nearest wall-mounted fire alarm located in the hallways near the exits and Phone the Campus Police, Local **4333**; report to Campus Police if anyone is suspected of being in the building after general evacuation.

6. Evacuate the room and building- if you can quickly find your coat (in winter) and personal belongings, take these with you. Leave everything else.

Chemical [or liquid solutions especially microorganisms] Spill

For a minor spill:

1. Alert your TA
2. Soak up the liquid in paper towels. Wear gloves.
3. Dispose of the contaminated towels in the appropriate waste container (ask your TA which container to use).

For a major spill:

Alert your TA. Your TA will decide to either evacuate the room and call Facilities Resources at Local **5301**, or to contain and clean up the spill with the special equipment provided in the prep room.

Equipment

Report broken or damaged equipment promptly to your TA or the course technician and describe the nature of the problem as best you can ("broken" or "not working" is not a sufficient description to diagnose a problem).

Report spills in/on equipment immediately to your TA or the course technician. Some chemicals will permanently damage the equipment if not cleaned up properly and quickly.

Glass and "Sharps"

1. Dispose of broken glass in the white buckets, and razor blades in the specially-marked "sharps/glass" containers. Please **do not put paper waste** in these "sharps" containers. Never throw glass into the garbage bins.
2. Use a brush and pan to sweep up broken glass. Ensure that all broken glass is cleaned up (brush and pan are in the prep room).
3. Report breakage of equipment to your instructor.

Handling Animals

Extra precautions must be taken when handling live organisms because of the potential of bites and scratches and the production of aerosols. Live organisms can also escape. In undergraduate labs, the animals being used will not knowingly be infected with human pathogens but natural infections may be present. The professor in charge of labs using animals or insects will advise TAs (and TAs will advise students) of potential biohazards and the proper way to handle this material.

Preparation (Prep) Rooms

Preparation rooms are not to be used by students except for emergency use. It may disrupt technical preparation and sensitive set-up.

BIO152 Laboratory 1:
Arthropod Diversity and Adaptation

The lab 1 assignment involves the completion of a group worksheet (found via the 'Labs' link on the course Blackboard site). The worksheet is due at the end of your lab (i.e., BEFORE you leave).

Overview

In this lab exercise, you will observe a variety of arthropod organisms. Your task is to identify some of the adaptations these organisms have evolved for their particular lifestyles, and to suggest hypotheses to explain some of their striking traits.

Preparation

1. Read through entire lab and associated worksheet(s).
2. Review textbook chapters 1 & 24.
3. Review Appendix 1: Scientific Investigation.

Laboratory Objectives

After completing this laboratory exercise, you should be able to:

1. Define "adaptation" and explain how it relates to evolution and the diversity of living organisms.
2. Appreciate the immense diversity in organisms, and insects in particular, and some of the key differences between representative species, such as metamorphosis, and feeding and mating strategies.
3. Compare and contrast adaptations for viability and adaptations for competition for mates and how each can help explain organismal diversity.
4. Derive evolutionary hypotheses based on observations of an organism's environment, structure, and lifestyle.

Background Information

Living organisms exhibit an astonishing variety of shapes, sizes, colours, organs, ways of life, and behaviours. All living forms, from bacteria to apes to mushrooms to trees, have descended from a common ancestor that appeared on Earth around 3 billion years ago. How these living forms diverged and diversified to their present forms is an important question for biological research.

Arthropods (*arthro* = joint; *pod* = leg) are animals with jointed legs, and consist of spiders, insects, and crustaceans. It is estimated that there are 1,100,000 species of arthropods (Table 1.1), the majority of which are insects. Insects are found in just about every habitat on Earth: in water and in soil, on plants and in the air, and in hot deserts and Arctic tundra. They exhibit a variety of lifestyles, behaviours, and bodily structures.

Adaptation

A **trait** (characteristic) of a living organism that contributes to fitness by improving the organism's chances of surviving or reproducing is called an **adaptation**. An adaptation can be a physical feature of the body (e.g., colour of the wings), or a behaviour (e.g., attraction to certain smells). Biologists use the term "adaptation" in two ways: (1) *An adaptation* (noun) is a trait (e.g., "A bat's wing *is an adaptation* for flight."). (2) *Adaptation* (noun), and *to adapt* (verb) refer to the evolutionary process through which such traits arise (e.g., "Bats acquired wings through *adaptation* to their environment." or "Bats *adapted* to their environment by evolving wings.").

The Origin of Adaptations

In his 1859 book *On the Origin of Species*, Charles Darwin proposed a mechanism for the process of adaptation: **natural selection**. A modern version of Darwin's theory is outlined below.

TABLE 1.1   An Overview of Major Animal Phyla

Group and Phylum	Common Name or Example Taxa	Estimated Number of Species	Group and Phylum	Common Name or Example Taxa	Estimated Number of Species
Porifera	Sponges	7 000	Phoronida	Horseshoe worms	20
Cnidaria	Jellyfish, corals, anemones, hydroids, sea fans	10 000	Ectoprocta	Ectoprocts	4 500
			Brachiopoda	Brachiopods; lamp shells	335
Ctenophora	Comb jellies	100	**Protostomes: Ecdysozoa**		
Acoelomorpha	Acoelomate worms	10	Nematoda	Roundworms	25 000
Protostomes (basal group)			Kinorhyncha	Kinorhynchs	150
Chaetognatha	Arrow worms	100	Nematomorpha	Hair worms	320
			Priapula	Priapulans	16
Protostomes: Lophotrochozoa			Onychophora	Velvet worms	110
Rotifera	Rotifers	1 800	Tardigrada	Water bears	800
Platyhelminthes	Flatworms	20 000	Arthropoda	Arthropods (spiders, insects, crustaceans)	1 100 000
Nemertea	Ribbon worms	900			
Gastrotricha	Gastrotrichs	450	**Deuterostomes**		
Acanthocephala	Acanthocephalans	1 100	Echinodermata	Echinoderms (sea stars, sea urchins, sea cucumbers)	7 000
Entoprocta	Entroprocts	150			
Gnathostomulida	Gnathostomulids	80			
Sipuncula	Peanut worms	320	Hemichordata	Acorn worms	85
Echiura	Spoon worms	135	Chordata	Chordates (tunicates, lancelets, sharks, bony fish, amphibians, reptiles, mammals)	50 000
Annelida	Segmented worms	16 500			
Mollusca	Molluscs (clams, snails, octopuses)	94 000			

Reprinted from *Biological Science Canadian Edition*, by Scott Freeman, Michael Harrington, and Joan C. Sharp (2011), Pearson Education, Canada.

Populations are made up of different individuals. In each generation, new traits and new combinations of traits are created in the population by **mutations** (genetic "errors"), as well as **recombination** (the mixing of genes through sex). The result is that some individuals invariably possess traits that help them to survive and reproduce better—and thus leave more offspring—than other individuals. Such individuals are said to have a higher **fitness**.

Natural selection results from variation among individuals in the number of surviving offspring they contribute to the next generation. If the traits that confer high fitness are **heritable** (i.e., passed in genes from parent to offspring), then these traits will be present in a greater proportion of individuals in the next generation. Natural selection and inheritance will be repeated in each generation, until the advantageous trait is present in almost every individual. This process—change over generations in the proportion of individuals with a certain trait—is called **evolution**. Thus, an adaptation is a fitness-enhancing trait that has spread through the population by natural selection. Complex adaptations, such as eyes, result from many such traits combined over many generations.

To summarize, in order for a trait to be considered an adaptation, the following three criteria must be met:

1. The trait is heritable.
2. There is variation for the trait.
3. Variation in the trait leads to some individuals leaving more offspring in the next generation than others, or having higher fitness.

Although this exercise is about adaptation, it is important to realize that not all traits are adaptations. Some traits are probably neutral for fitness (e.g., the colour of your hair) and not all differences between populations result from natural selection. Populations also change genetically by random processes (**genetic drift**), or by the influx of migrants from other populations (**gene flow**). Thus, some differences between populations may not be adaptations, but simply changes accumulated over many generations.

Whether or not a particular trait is or is not an adaptation is not always obvious. To understand the evolutionary process that gave rise to a particular trait, it is often necessary to consider the **phylogeny** (evolutionary history and relationships) of the species in question. Knowledge of the phylogeny may enable biologists to determine when and in what sequence different traits evolved. For the purposes of this lab, however, we will assume that any complex structure, or any trait that appears to benefit the organism, is an adaptation.

The Process of Adaptation: Some Hypotheses

When biologists observe an interesting trait that appears to be an adaptation, they often come up with at least one **hypothesis** of how the trait may have increased the fitness of individuals possessing that trait. In other words, they come up with a possible *function* for the trait that might explain why the trait evolved. The hypothesis is often inspired by some knowledge of the organism's habitat, behaviour, and lifestyle. Once a hypothesis has been formulated, the next step is to *test* it (see the boxed text on next page).

A few hypotheses that are used to explain adaptations in many different organisms are outlined in the next two pages. These are divided into adaptations for **viability** (i.e., success in survival and acquisition of food) and adaptations for **competition for mates**. A particular adaptation can, of course, enhance both viability and competition for mates (keen vision might be an example). Alternatively, some traits may have opposing effects on viability and competition for mates.

Testing a Hypothesis

A scientific hypothesis is a tentative answer to a question about the natural world. Hypotheses must be tested because, ideally, all scientific ideas and explanations are evaluated by how well they conform to empirical (i.e., tangible) evidence. Unless it is supported by empirical evidence, a hypothesis is just a guess. A concept map to illustrate hypotheses and the scientific method can be found in Appendix 1.

Testing a hypothesis about the function of a particular adaptation usually involves observations or experiments to determine whether or not the trait serves the suggested function. For example, the hypothesis that the green colour of a particular species of insect is an adaptation for camouflage can be tested by painting 50 individuals another colour (the "painted") and painting 50 other individuals (the "controls") with transparent paint, and counting the number of painted and control individuals that are eaten by predators over a given period of time.

Observations or experiments generate data, which are usually analyzed statistically to determine whether or not the patterns in the data are likely to have come about by chance alone. (For example, what could you conclude if 20 control and 24 painted individuals were eaten?) If the resulting empirical evidence is consistent with the hypothesis, it is said to support the hypothesis. If the evidence is not consistent with the hypothesis, the hypothesis is said to be rejected. However, few tests are totally conclusive, and thus a number of independent tests are often required.

Adaptations for Viability

Adaptations for locomotion (movement), predator or parasite avoidance, food acquisition, shelter construction, and tolerance of ambient conditions (e.g., cold, heat, drought) all increase an organism's viability. An individual that fails to survive or obtain food will produce no offspring and have a fitness of zero. Natural selection arising from variation in viability is called **viability selection**. Some examples of adaptations for viability are illustrated in Figure 1.1.

Adaptations for Competition for Mates

An individual's fitness depends not only on how long it survives and how well it locates food, but also on how successful it is in competing for mates. An individual that fails to mate will produce no offspring and have a fitness of zero. Natural selection arising from variable mating success is called **sexual selection**.

Sexual selection often results in the evolution of differences between males and females in **secondary sexual characteristics** (i.e., sexual characteristics other than ovaries and testes). Such a difference between the sexes in the shape or size of the body is called **sexual dimorphism**. In some cases, a structure appears in fully functional form in one sex, but is also present

(A)   **(B)**   **(C)**

Courtesy of Biopix.

Figure 1.1
(A) Camouflage: Organisms may benefit by physically resembling their environment, making them less visible to predators. Pink-winged grasshoppers (*Bryodema tuberculata*) blend in well with their surroundings; their colouration may be an adaptation to avoid predation. **(B) Life in water:** Many organisms possess special adaptations for life in water. Aquatic insects often have bodies and legs specially shaped to facilitate locomotion in their aquatic environment, as do some semiaquatic mammals. For example, the North American River Otter (*Lontra canadensis*) has webbed toes, a streamlined body, and a tapered tail. **(C) Feeding:** Many insects have adapted to particular diets by evolving specialized mouthparts. For example ants have powerful jaws (mandibles) for biting and tearing, mosquitoes (shown above) have a tube (stylet) for piercing and sucking, and butterflies have a long "tongue" (proboscis) for lapping up nectar from flowers.

in miniature, non-functional form in the other sex. This occurs because males and females share nearly all of their genes, so that selection acting on one sex only will usually also affect the other sex to some degree. (For example, why do male humans have nipples?) Two principal mechanisms of sexual selection are intrasexual competition and mate choice.

(A)   **(B)**

Figure 1.2
(A) Intrasexual Competition: In many species of animals, males fight with males for access to females. A male that is able to defeat his rivals in combat will probably sire more offspring. For this reason, male animals often possess adaptations for fighting, such as horns, mandibles, or tusks. In some species, these "weapons" take on very impressive (sometimes bizarre!) proportions. Male European earwigs (*Forficula auricularia*) have large projections from their abdomen (forceps; shown above), which they use in competition with other males. Female earwigs have much smaller forceps. **(B) Mate Choice:** In many species, females and/or males are choosy about their mates. Mate choice is thought to increase the fitness of the "chooser" by enabling it to mate only with healthy individuals (which are thus more "attractive" as mates). Because attractive individuals tend to acquire more mates, they usually produce more offspring. Thus, many animals have adapted to the preferences of the opposite sex by evolving elaborate structures, colour patterns, and courtship displays that might reveal their health and vigour. For example, female peahens choose male peacocks (shown above) based on their elaborate feathered display.

ACTIVITY 1.1

Arthropod Observation and Identification of Adaptations

THIS PART OF THE LAB IS DONE IN GROUPS OF 4

Description:

In this exercise, you will have a chance to examine organisms native to Ontario and to global regions, including Madagascar and Vietnam. Your task is to identify some of the adaptations these insects have evolved for their particular lifestyles, and to suggest hypotheses to explain some of their striking traits.

Use the hypotheses outlined above and the information in **Appendix 1** as a guide. In many cases there is no "right answer" because the "true" functions of these traits are not known. However, coming up with a good hypothesis (which can then be tested) is the first step. Note that when developing your questions, hypotheses, experiments and predictions, try not to over-complicate things; think methodically and focus on one trait at a time.

Science is a collaborative activity, so discuss and debate your ideas with your classmates!

Materials:

Magnifying glass
Organism specimens, including:
Mealworms and mealworm beetles (*Tenebrio molitor*)
Madagascar Hissing Cockroach (*Gromphadorhina portentosa*)
Sowbugs (Order: Isopoda)
Butterfly specimens, including Monarch butterflies (*Danaus plexippus*) and butterflies from the following families: Pieridae, Nymphalidae, and Hesperiidae.
Beetle specimens,
Stick insects

Procedure:

1. Several different sets of specimens will be available in the lab. Each group of 4 people will take turns observing each set of specimens around the lab room.
2. Read the information provided on the following pages and examine each insect in the set with a magnifying lens. You may handle some of the live insects under your TA's supervision; do not remove them from their cages without consulting your TA first. Observe the preserved insects inside their boxes.
3. For each specimen you have been given a possible experimental question regarding a structural or behavioural trait possessed by the

specimen. Develop a hypothesis for how a structural or behavioural trait mentioned in the experimental question is an adaptation to the insect's habitat/environment and lifestyle.

4. Consider how you might test your hypothesis. Can it be tested by observations alone? What would you need to observe? If an experiment is required, how would you set it up? If your hypothesis is correct, what are your predicted (expected) results?

5. Complete the Lab 1 Worksheet (due before you leave the lab).

Mealworms and mealworm beetles (*Tenebrio molitor*)

The mealworm beetle (*Tenebrio molitor*) is a holometabolic insect that has four life stages, including egg, larva, pupa, and adult. The length of the life cycle is three to five months. "Mealworms" are in the larval stage of the mealworm beetle life cycle. The larval stage is distinguished by multiple (9-20) molting events. In the pupa stage, the organism starts off creamy white, but then darkens prior to emergence of the adult. The adult is black with hardened front wings. Mealworms and mealworm beetles eat a diet consisting of decaying matter (including leaves, grasses, and insects), new plant growth, feces, and stored grains.

Possible experimental question: Why do adult *Tenebrio* have a hardened exterior?

Madagascar Hissing Cockroaches

Cockroaches belong to the order Blattodea. Although some are common pests in human dwellings, many of the over 3500 known species of cockroaches are not associated with humans. As their name suggests, these hissing cockroaches are native to the island of Madagascar, where they live in forested areas. Hissing cockroaches feed on a variety of vegetable matter on the forest floor. Adult males are larger than females, and possess prominent bumps on the dorsal pro-thorax (anterior section of the thorax) that serve as a plate that protects the head. Males often defend territories, fending off rivals by lunging at them and pushing them away. Although they do not bite, adults of both sexes hiss when handled or pursued. They are preyed upon by birds, mammals, reptiles, amphibians and other insects. Adult males also hiss during aggressive encounters, and during courtship and mating. One adult male will defend a territory around several females. Females carry their eggs in a pouch (ootheca) until they hatch.

Possible experimental question: Do the bumps on the dorsal pro-thorax of male Madagascar hissing cockroaches provide an advantage when competing for mates?

Sowbugs

Sowbugs or pillbugs are terrestrial crustaceans belonging to the order Isopoda. There are more than 10,000 isopod species that have been identified. The word "isopod" comes from the Greek word for "same" (*iso*) and "foot" (*podos*). Female isopods lay their eggs directly into their brood pouch, where the young hatch, develop, and moult. A distinguishing characteristic of isopods is that they engage in biphasic moulting (meaning "two-phases") to replace their exoskeleton; one half of the body moults before the other.

Possible experimental question: Does the egg-laying behavior of female isopods provide a survival advantage for the offspring?

Butterflies

The order Lepidoptera (moths and butterflies) is one of the largest insect orders in terms of number of species. The collection of Ontario butterflies seen in Lab 1 includes Monarch butterflies (*Danaus plexippus*) and butterflies from the following families: Pieridae, Nymphalidae, and Hesperiidae. Monarch butterflies have an effective chemical defense. When they feed on milkweed plants they isolate poisonous cardenolides in the milkweed that are poisonous to their predators.

During their lives, all butterflies undergo a series of profound changes in body form, behaviour, and lifestyle, a process known as **complete metamorphosis**. The tiny *eggs* hatch into *larvae* (caterpillars) which, in most species, feed on vegetation and grow. When a caterpillar attains full size, it assumes a dormant and nearly immobile form called a *pupa*. Inside the pupa's protective cocoon, the caterpillar develops into an *adult*. When its transformation is complete, the adult butterfly breaks out of the cocoon and dries its wings. Unlike the larva, the adult butterfly feeds on nectar from flowers and reproduces.

Possible experimental question: The chemical defense possessed by Monarch butterflies (described above) does not help a particular Monarch after a predator has already tried to eat it. How do Monarchs warn off predators to prevent being killed?

Beetles

Beetles (order Coleoptera) are thought to be the largest insect order. In fact, beetles are thought to comprise nearly a quarter of all animal species on earth. In this lab, you will observe various beetle specimens. Please refer to the specimen labels for species identification. Beetles undergo complete metamorphosis. Many beetles display interesting mating behaviours that may involve the release of pheromones or physical aggression and combat. Please take note of morphological differences between males and females.

Possible experimental question: What trait in one of the species of beetles observed in lab may help males better compete for mates?

Walkingstick Insects

Walkingsticks belong to the order Phasmatodea (stick insects); the ordinal name originates from the Latin word *phasma*, meaning "ghost". Most of the 2000 species of walkingsticks are found in the tropics. Adult and juvenile (nymph) stick insects feed on leaves. In one species, males are known to prefer longer females as mates, probably because longer females tend to produce more and larger eggs. Copulation can last over 100 hours in some species. Females are capable of parthenogenesis (asexual reproduction); parthenogenic eggs take longer to develop than fertilized eggs. Stick insects are preyed upon by birds and small mammals.

Possible experimental question: What is the most likely explanation for the peculiar appearance of the stick insect?

Other Specimens

In lab, you will be able to observe some additional live arthropod specimens. Closely examine some of the structures and behaviours of these specimens. Do these specimens have any similarities to the arthropods described in your lab manual? Do you think that some of these traits are adaptive? Think of some experimental questions about the observed features and/or behaviours of these specimens. How would you go about answering these questions (i.e., develop a hypothesis, design an experiment, state your predictions, etc.).

References:

Aguinaldo, A.M., J.M. Turbeville, L.S. Linford, M.C. Rivera, J.R. Garey, R.A. Raff, and J.A. Lake. Evidence for a Clade of Nematodes, Arthropods, and other Moulting Animals." Nature, 1997: 489-493.

Hennemann, F.H., and O.V. Conle. 2008. Revision of Oriental Phasmatodea: The tribe Pharnaciini Gunther, 1953, including the description of the world's longest insect, and a survey of the family Phasmatidae Gray, 1835 with keys to the subfamilies and tribes (Phasmatodea: "Anareolatae": Phasmatidae). Zootaxa, 1906: 1-311.

Stork, N.E. 1997. Measuring global biodiversity and its decline. Pages 41-68 in Biodiversity II: Understanding and Protecting Our Biological Resources (Reaka-Kudla, M.L., Wilson, D.E., and E.O. Wilson, editors). Joseph Henry Press, Washington, D.C.

Acknowledgments:

The lab was adapted, with permission, from: Goldman, C.A., and J. Wheeler. 2010. BIO120: Adaptation & Biodiversity Laboratory Manual. Department of Ecology and Evolutionary Biology, University of Toronto, and Russell Bonduriansky.

Photo Credits:
Earwig and river otter photo by J.C. Schou, from www.biopix.com
Mosquito photo by G. Drange, from www.biopix.com
Grasshopper and peacock photo by N. Sloth, from www.biopix.com

UTM Biology Faculty Profile:

Excavation site in South Africa
(Picture courtesy of prof. Reisz)

Dr. Robert Reisz is a vertebrate paleontologist studying the anatomy and evolutionary relationships of Paleozoic vertebrates, including the distant ancestors to modern amphibians, reptiles and mammals.

Recent Publications:

- Reisz, R. R., Evans, D. C, Roberts, E. M., Sues, H-D., Yates, A. M. (2012) Oldest known dinosaurian nesting site and the reproductive biology of the Early Jurassic sauropodomorph *Massospondylus*. *Proceedings of the National Academy of Science* 109: 2428-2433 (PNAS-weekly highlight)

- Fröbisch, N. B. and Reisz R. R. (2012) A new species of dissorophid (*Cacops woehri*) from the Lower Permian Dolese Quarry, near Richards Spur, Oklahoma. *Journal of Vertebrate Paleontology* 32: 35-44.

- Tsuji, L. A., Müller, J., and Reisz, R. R. (2012) Anatomy of *Emeroleter levis* and the phylogeny of the nycteroleter parareptiles. *Journal of Vertebrate Paleontology* 32: 45-67.

- Modesto, S., Smith, R., Campione, N., and Reisz, R. R. (2011) The last "pelycosaur": a varanopid synapsid from the *Pristerognathus* Assemblage Zone, Middle Permian of South Africa. *Naturwissenschaften* 98: 1027-1034. (with cover illustration)

- Reisz, R. R., Scott, D., and Modesto, S. P. (2011) A new Early Permian reptile and its significance in early diapsid evolution. *Proceedings of the Royal Society of London, Series B.* 278: 3731-3737.

For more information about Dr. Reisz's lab, research and publications, visit his website at:

http://www.utm.utoronto.ca/~w3reisz/

BIO152 Laboratory 2
Isolating DNA

The lab 2 assignment involves the completion of an individual assignment (assignment details and templates are found via the 'Labs' link on the course Blackboard site). Your assignment is due at the beginning of Lab 3 (i.e., next week).

Overview

Deoxyribonucleic acid (DNA) houses the genetic information of all organisms within varying sequences of four nucleotides (adenine, thymine, guanine, and cytosine). Discrete sections of DNA known as genes are the basic units of heredity or "blueprints" that make organisms. In eukaryotic cells, DNA is packaged with proteins and this DNA-protein complex is commonly found in a threadlike form called chromatin, which forms chromosomes. In this laboratory exercise, you will extract DNA from split pea cells to see this molecule for yourself.

Preparation

1. Read through the entire lab and associated assignment details.
2. Review textbook chapters 2 & 4.

Laboratory Objectives

After completing this laboratory exercise, you should be able to:

1. List the basic steps involved in extracting DNA
2. Explain the rationale for each step in the extraction procedure
3. Describe how DNA can be extracted from cells
4. Determine the answer to this question:

> **What is the effect on the quantity, quality and purity of extracted DNA when one of the steps in the extraction procedure is altered?**

Background Information

DNA extraction, or isolation, has become a routine procedure to enable the collection of DNA that can be used in subsequent experimental procedures or analyses, such as gel electrophoresis, polymerase chain reaction (PCR) and cloning. DNA extraction involves four basic steps:

1. Lysing the cellular and nuclear membranes
2. Separating cellular material from DNA
3. Protecting DNA from degradation
4. Precipitating DNA from solution

Lysing plant and bacterial cells first involves breaking down the cell wall using either chemical or mechanical means such as grinding or blending. During this process, the cell and/or nuclear membranes may also be disrupted to some extent. The bulk cellular material can be removed by straining.

Once the cell wall has been disrupted and the bulk material removed, the remaining cellular and nuclear membranes need to be lysed. This is achieved by the use of detergent. The standard DNA extraction procedure for this lab uses a detergent containing sodium laureth sulphate. Sodium laureth sulphate is found in many liquid cleaning products (e.g., dish detergent, laundry detergent, shampoos and body washes) and cleans by removing fats and proteins. In our DNA extraction procedure, the sodium laureth sulphate breaks apart the fats and proteins of phospholipid bilayer of the cellular and nuclear membranes forming micelles (little soapy balls) with the membrane lipids and proteins, effectively separating the membranes from the DNA.

When the DNA no longer has the protection of the nuclear membrane, it can be at risk of degradation by cellular nucleases (enzymes that break down DNA and RNA). Some experimental protocols will try to limit this nuclease activity by conducting all of the steps at cold temperatures as this will slow down the enzymes (note the use of cold water used during the "blending" step in our lab protocol). Nuclease activity can be further limited by adding proteases to the reaction mixture. Proteases are enzymes that break down proteins and with thus destroy the unwanted nucleases that might degrade the DNA. In addition to destroying the nucleases, the proteases may help increase the purity of the extracted DNA by breaking down other cellular proteins. Our standard procedure calls for the use of a powdered meat tenderizer as our source of proteases. However, proteases are also found in pineapple juice and contact lens cleaners.

Now that the DNA has been separated from the other cellular material, the DNA needs to be precipitated from the solution. This step is achieved using ice-cold alcohol with the help of the salt added earlier in the procedure. DNA is readily soluble in water because of the negatively charged phosphate group carried by each nucleotide. To help stabilize the DNA, salt may be added to the solution. The positively charged sodium ions from the salt are attracted to the negatively charged phosphate groups effectively neutralizing the DNA's electric charge allowing the long DNA molecules to aggregate together and to disassociate from cellular proteins. Alcohol is less dense than water and will stay on top of the watery reaction mixture below. When the ice-cold ethanol is added, the positively charged sodium is replaced with carbons from the ethanol causing the DNA to clump together. The DNA precipitates at the water/ethanol interface because DNA is not soluble in ethanol.

When your DNA extractions are done, the appearance of your final product may vary. If your DNA has remained intact (i.e., you have effectively minimized breakdown by using gentle mixing procedures and limiting nuclease activity), you should be able to observe long, thin, strands floating in the ethanol layer. If your DNA has broken down at some point during the procedure (e.g., due to nuclease activity or over-enthusiastic mixing), your DNA may appear as a "fluffy" white substance floating in the ethanol layer; this is not the best result but at least you can still see your DNA. Extremely pure DNA (i.e., not contaminated with cellular proteins or other cellular materials) will be almost transparent and jelly-like (it is very unlikely that your DNA will appear this pure). Your DNA will likely be various shades of off-white. The whiter your DNA is, the higher the purity.

ACTIVITY 2.1

DNA Extraction from Split Peas

Description:

In pairs, **each student** will run the standard procedure. After both students have run the standard procedure to extract the split pea DNA, one student of the pair will run the procedure again altering one reagent (see Table 2.1) and the other student will run the procedure using the negative control for that reagent. You will then compare the yield and visual characteristics of the crude DNA that was extracted for each protocol.

Materials:

1. Split peas
2. Table salt
3. Cold Tap water
4. Liquid dish detergent
5. Meat tenderizer
6. Cold 95% ethanol, cold 50% ethanol
7. Additional materials –tubes with caps, blender, measuring cup, strainer, timer, wooden stick or glass probe, plastic spoon, 1 ml plastic pipettes, 1/8 measuring teaspoon

Standard Procedure:
(adapted from: http://learn.genetics.utah.edu)

1. One person at each bench will prepare the split pea mixture for the entire bench. Measure out 100 g of split peas, 1/8 teaspoon of table salt, and 250 mL of cold tap water. Put the mixture in a blender, put the top on the blender, and blend on high for 30 seconds.
2. Pour your thin pea-cell soup through a strainer into the measuring cup provided. The solid bits left in the strainer should be discarded.
3. Pour 15 mL of the strained mixture from the measuring cup into <u>eight</u> test tubes, one for each member of the bench.

4. Add 1 mL of liquid dish detergent to the strained mixture in your test tube and GENTLY rock the solution intermittently for 5 minutes.
5. Add a pinch of meat tenderizer to each test tube and **stir gently**. Be careful! If you stir too hard, you'll break up the DNA, making it harder to see.
6. **Slowly** add the cold 95% ethanol down the side of the tube, tilting the tube. Add about the same volume of alcohol as your watery soup mixture. The alcohol will form a layer at the surface of the pea mixture. Do not mix these two layers together. Use a wooden applicator stick to bring some of the DNA-containing water mixture up into the alcohol to precipitate more DNA. KEEP your extracted DNA to compare the standard procedure results to your chosen altered procedure in step 7 below.
7. As a pair, you will now perform an alternate version of the standard procedure and a negative control. All other steps in the protocol should be unchanged (see Table 2.1).
8. Examine your extracted DNA from each version of your experiment and record your observations in Table 2.2. You will use this information to complete your lab assignment.

Table 2.1
Alternative protocol

Standard Procedure Reagent	Substitution	Negative Control
Cold 95% ethanol	Cold 50% ethanol	Cold Water

Table 2.2
Comparison of DNA extraction procedure results

	Standard Procedure	Alternate Procedure	Negative Control
Reagent Used:	ethanol 95%	50% ethanol	Cold Water
Yield of DNA 1=lowest yield 2=mid yield 3=highest yield	3	2	1
Quality of DNA (Do you see intact strands or is your DNA "fluffy")	cloudy/ cluster form of DNA	strands of DNA	low quality
Purity of DNA (comment on the colour/clarity of your DNA)	white		

Check Your Understanding:

1. What are the four major steps involved in extracting DNA?
2. What is the purpose of each step in the protocol?
3. What might happen if you forgot to add the salt to your reaction mixture before blending?
4. Would you expect your DNA to be more pure or less pure when meat tenderizer is added? Explain.
5. Let's say that you did not tilt your test tube when pouring in the alcohol and the alcohol was able to mix with the watery mixture instead of forming a layer on top. What effect would this have on your extraction of DNA?

Apply What You Know:

As so popularly seen on television crime dramas such as CSI, criminals will sometimes use bleach as a means to clean up the crime scene. But not only does this criminal want to clean up the evidence of the crime but he or she probably wants to destroy the evidence that he or she was present at the crime scene by destroying any DNA evidence contained in blood smears or other bodily fluids. Why does bleach destroy DNA?

Why Is This Important?

DNA extraction is a relatively new biological technique and is used with other DNA technologies in all areas of biology. DNA extraction and other DNA technologies have numerous practical applications, and here are just a few:

- Genetic Engineering in Plants—has led to increased nutritional value, resistance of plants to pests and disease, as well as increased tolerance to environmental factors such as drought or heat.

- Genetic Engineering in Animals—has led to the production of animal clones, like Dolly the sheep, as well as genetically mutant strains of fruit flies used in research. Genetic engineering in animals has also lead to the treatment of some genetic disorders through gene therapy.

- Pharmaceuticals—development of drugs made using recombinant genetics, such as insulin.

- Paternity Testing—to verify that two individuals are biologically related.

- Forensic Identification—comparison of samples taken from the crime scene can be compared to identify suspects or even exonerate individuals wrongly accused of a crime.

- Medical Diagnosis—genetic testing can be done to determine if a person has a disease or is a carrier of a genetic disorder and may pass it down to his/her children. Examples include sickle-cell anemia, Down's syndrome, and Huntington's disease.

- Endangered species and illegal trade—to assist in monitoring the illegal trade of animals and wildlife products.

• Evolution, human migration, and origin—to determine how human populations have moved over time and how we have evolved over time to become who we are today.

Current Investigations and Applications:

• There are numerous unanswered questions in the realm of DNA research. Even though we understand the structure of DNA, how eukaryotic DNA is organized into chromosomes, and how DNA replicates, research is still ongoing in these areas. For instance, why is there such variation in the size of genomes? For example, the puffer fish genome is 400 million bases, while the locust genome is 9.3 gigabases!

• As you know, mutations that confer some advantage can be inherited, but what about non-mutational changes? How are these inherited? Epigenetics is the study of these heritable changes in appearance or gene expression caused by something other than modifications in the DNA sequence. An example of such a change is DNA methylation, which is a post-translational modification that suppresses gene expression without altering gene sequences.

• There are also several unanswered questions regarding the evolutionary relationship between DNA and RNAlike why might viruses have RNA instead of DNA?

Additional Resources:

To help you visualize what you will be doing in lab, look at the following:
1. DNA extraction virtual lab demonstrating DNA extraction from human cheek cells
   http://learn.genetics.utah.edu/units/biotech/extraction/

2. Science Online –introduction to Otzi the iceman, the 5000 year old frozen mummy with videos of the extraction found on UTube:
   The story of Otzi the Iceman is used to introduce a DNA extraction lab. Einkorn wheat was found on the cloak of this 5000 year old Neolithic warrior. http://www.youtube.com/watch?v=p3OzDndzcxs
   This video includes step-by-step instructions for extracting DNA from wheat. http://www.youtube.com/watch?v=iyb7fwduuGM

References:
Bloom, M.V., G.A. Freyer, and D.A. Micklos. *Laboratory DNA Science*. Menlo Park, CA: Benjamin Cummings, 1996.

Russel, P.J. *iGenetics: A Molecular Approach*, 3rd ed. San Francisco, CA: Benjamin Cummings, 2009.

UTM Biology Faculty Profile

Dr. Steven Short is an assistant Professor in the Department of Biology at UTM and is a faculty member in the Department of Ecology and Evolutionary Biology at the University of Toronto. Dr. Short's research focus is the molecular ecology of aquatic microorganisms, in particular phytoplankton, and how viruses affect phytoplankton ecology. In his research, Dr. Short utilizes DNA extraction to collect DNA for subsequent molecular analysis such as quantitative Polymerase Chain Reaction, or qPCR.

Recent Publications:

Short, C.M., Rusanova, O., Short, S.M. 2011. Quantification of virus genes provides evidence for seed-bank populations of phycodnaviruses in Lake Ontario, Canada. *The ISME Journal*, 5: 810-821.

Short, S.M., Rusanova, O., Staniewski, M.A. 2011. Novel Phycodnavirus genes amplified from Canadian freshwater environments. *Aquatic Microbial Ecology*, 63: 61-67.

Short, S.M., Short, C.M. 2009. Quantitative PCR reveals transient and persistent algal virus in Lake Ontario, Canada. *Environmental Microbiology*, 11(10): 2639-2648.

For more information about Dr. Short's lab, research and publications, visit his website at:

http://utm.utoronto.ca/biology/people/short-steven-m

BIO152 Laboratory 3
Mitosis and Meiosis

The lab 3 assignment involves the completion of a group worksheet (found via the 'Labs' link on the course Blackboard site). The worksheet is due at the end of your lab (i.e., BEFORE you leave).

Overview

The process of mitosis allows cells to give rise to new cells that have identical chromosome copies from the parent cell. The process of meiosis allows this genetic information to be passed from one generation to the next generation by distributing chromosomes into gametes. In this lab, you will become familiar with the processes of mitosis and meiosis and learn to identify specific mitotic and meiotic phases.

Preparation

1. Read through the entire lab and associated worksheet(s).
2. Review textbook chapters 11 & 12.

Laboratory Objectives

After completing this laboratory exercise, you should be able to:
1. Describe and identify all phases of mitosis and meiosis.
2. Describe differences between mitosis and cytokinesis in plant and animal cells.
3. Describe differences between mitosis and meiosis.
4. Explain the purpose of mitosis and meiosis and where they take place in organisms.
5. Operate a compound light microscope.

Background Information
Introduction

The nuclei in cells of eukaryotic organisms contain chromosomes with clusters of **genes,** discrete units of hereditary information consisting of duplicated deoxyribonucleic acid (DNA). Structural proteins in the chromosomes organize the DNA and participate in DNA folding and condensation. When cells divide, chromosomes and genes are duplicated and passed on to daughter cells. Single-celled organisms divide for reproduction. Multicellular organisms have reproductive cells (eggs or sperm), but they also have somatic (body) cells that divide for growth or replacement.

In somatic cells and single-celled organisms, the nucleus divides by **mitosis** into two daughter nuclei, which have the same number of chromosomes and the same genes as the parent cell. For example, the epidermis or outer layer of skin tissue is continuously being replaced through cell reproduction involving mitosis. All of these new skin cells are genetically identical. Yeast and amoeba are both single-celled organisms that can reproduce asexually through mitotic divisions to form additional organisms—genetically identical clones.

Cancerous cells are characterized by uncontrolled mitotic and cell division, and therefore, the study of mitosis and its regulation is key to developing new cancer treatments. In 2009, three scientists studying chromosomes and the regulation of mitosis were awarded the Nobel Prize in medicine for their discovery of **telomeres.** Telomeres are DNA sequences on the ends of chromosomes that become shorter during every mitotic cycle of somatic cells. Without telomeres protecting the chromosome ends, important genes located at the ends of chromosomes might be lost in mitosis. The loss of telomeres in each division of somatic cells may be one of many regulatory mechanisms that limit the number of mitotic cycles that cells can undergo. If telomeres fail to shorten, cells may continue to divide, as in cancer cells.

In multicellular organisms, in preparation for sexual reproduction, a type of nuclear division called **meiosis** takes place. In meiosis, certain cells in ovaries or testes (or sporangia in plants) divide twice, but the chromosomes only replicate once. This process results in the four daughter nuclei with new combinations of chromosomes. Eggs or sperm (or spores in plants) are eventually formed. In contrast to mitosis, the process of meiosis contributes to the genetic variation that is important in sexual reproduction. Generally in both mitosis and meiosis, after nuclear division the cytoplasm divides, a process called **cytokinesis.**

Events from the beginning of one cell division to the beginning of the next are collectively called the **cell cycle.** The cell cycle is divided into two major phases: interphase and mitotic phase (M). The M phase represents the division of the nucleus and cytoplasm (Figure 3.1).

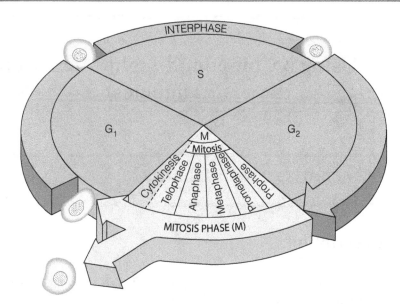

Figure 3.1.
The cell cycle. In interphase (G_1, S, G_2), DNA replication and most of the cell's growth and biochemical activity take place. In the M phase, the nucleus divides in mitosis, and the cytoplasm divides in cytokinesis. *Reprinted from Investigating Biology Lab Manual, Seventh Edition, by Jane B. Reece, et.al. (2011), Benjamin Cummings, a Pearson Education Company.*

Reprinted from *Investigating Biology Lab Manual*, Seventh Edition, by Jane B. Reece, et al. (2011), Benjamin Cummings, a Pearson Education Company.

ACTIVITY 3.1
Using a Compound Light Microscope
(~10 minutes)

THIS ACTIVITY IS DONE INDIVIDUALLY

Description:

In this activity you will familiarizes yourself with using a compound light microscope (Figure 3.2).

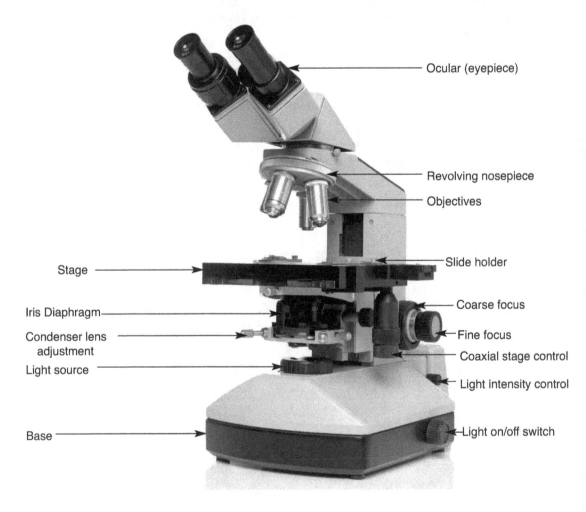

Figure 3.2.
Parts of a compound light microscope.
Courtesy of Shutterstock.

Materials:

1. Prepared slides.
2. Compound microscope.

Procedure:

1. Ensure that your work area is clean and uncluttered.
2. Record the number on the bench in front of you. This corresponds to the microscope in the cabinet that you will use.
   Your Microscope # _____
3. Carefully remove the microscope from the cabinet and place it on the bench. Carry the microscope close to your body in an upright position with one hand placed under the base and the other hand holding the arm.
4. After obtaining a microscope from the cabinet, do not drag the microscope across the table. Doing so can damage the intricate optics and mechanisms of the microscope.
5. Identify the parts of your compound microscope shown in Figure 3.2.
6. Carefully clean the ocular and objectives with *lens paper only*. If a smudge or scratch persists, consult the TA.
7. Make sure that the microscope was stored with the scanning objective (4X) is in place (i.e., it is pointing down). Never begin a session with the high power objective in place. If necessary, use the revolving nosepiece ring to click the low power objective in place.
8. Inspect the electric cord, making sure that it is not frayed or damaged. Plug in the electric cord as instructed so it will not get in your way, trip other students or damage the microscope. Turn the switch to the "on" position.
9. Completely **lower the stage** using the **course adjustment knob** BEFORE you place your slide on the stage.
10. Carefully place your slide on the stage (your TA will let you know which slide you should start with) and use the **slide holder** to hold it in place.
11. Use the **stage coaxial stage adjustment knobs** to roughly align the specimen (on the slide) with the condenser lens below. The condenser lens directs the light through the specimen to the objective lens.
12. Adjust the **distance between the oculars** to match the distance between your pupils. One of the oculars on the microscope can be focused individually for precision using a Diopter rings (located on each ocular). If you are having difficulty adjusting your eyepieces, consult the TA.
13. Use the **coarse adjustment knob** to **focus the specimen**. *This knob is to be used to view specimens under scanning (4X) and low power (10X) only.* Practice your microscopy skills by viewing various parts of the slide. While viewing the slide, do not rest your hand on the stage.
14. **Reposition the slide** using the **coaxial stage adjustment knobs** to attain the desired view. Use the **iris diaphragm** and **condenser** to focus and regulate the light entering the microscope. On scanning and low power, fine adjustment knob may be used to fine tune the specimen.
15. Using the revolving nosepiece ring rotate the high power objective (40X) into position. You should be able to feel the objective click into place.

16. Your microscopes are **parcentric** and **parfocal**. This means that if an object is centered and in sharp focus with one objective, it will be centered and in focus when another objective is rotated into the viewing position and require only minor adjustments in focusing. Using the **fine adjustments knob** only, focus your specimen. You may have to reposition your specimen carefully to the center and adjust the **iris diaphragm** and **condenser**.

ACTIVITY 3.2

Observing Mitosis and Cytokinesis in Plant and Animal Cells (~20 minutes)

THIS ACTIVITY IS DONE INDIVIDUALLY

In this activity you will observe the stages of mitosis in onion root tip cells (plants) and whitefish blastula cells (animal). An overview of mitosis can be seen in Figure 3.3.

ACTIVITY 3.2.1

Observing Mitosis and Cytokinesis in Plant Cells

Description:

When observing the prepared onion root tip slide, you should note that, unlike animal cells, plant cells have no centrioles. Also note that plants have cell walls (in addition to the cell membranes found in animals) that result in some differences in the process of cytokinesis when compared to animals.

Materials:

1. Prepared slides of onion root tip
2. Compound microscope

Figure 3.3

Interphase and mitosis in an animal cell.

Reprinted from iGenetics: A Molecular Approach, Third Edition, by Peter J. Russell (2010), Benjamin Cummings, a Pearson Education Company

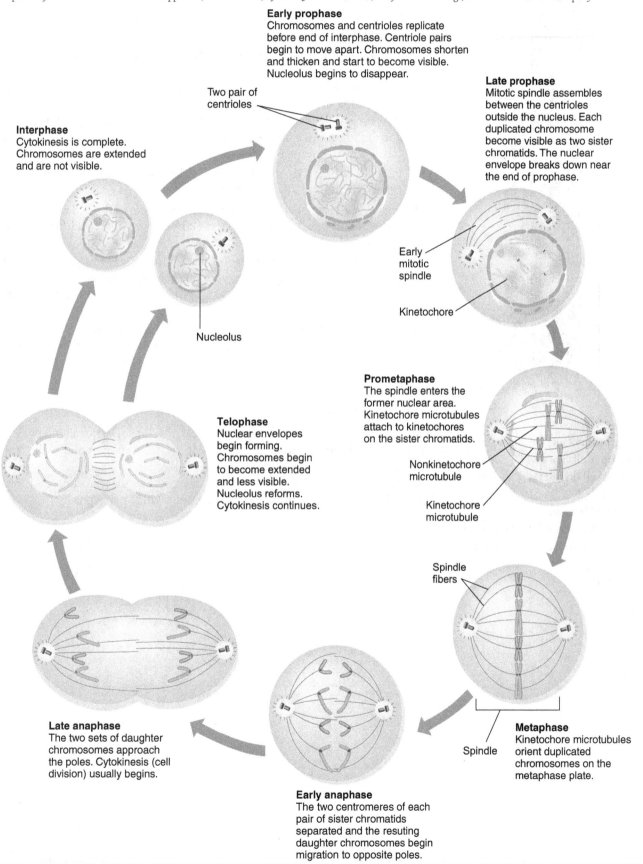

Early prophase
Chromosomes and centrioles replicate before end of interphase. Centriole pairs begin to move apart. Chromosomes shorten and thicken and start to become visible. Nucleolus begins to disappear.

Late prophase
Mitotic spindle assembles between the centrioles outside the nucleus. Each duplicated chromosome become visible as two sister chromatids. The nuclear envelope breaks down near the end of prophase.

Two pair of centrioles

Interphase
Cytokinesis is complete. Chromosomes are extended and are not visible.

Early mitotic spindle

Kinetochore

Nucleolus

Prometaphase
The spindle enters the former nuclear area. Kinetochore microtubules attach to kinetochores on the sister chromatids.

Telophase
Nuclear envelopes begin forming. Chromosomes begin to become extended and less visible. Nucleolus reforms. Cytokinesis continues.

Nonkinetochore microtubule

Kinetochore microtubule

Spindle fibers

Late anaphase
The two sets of daughter chromosomes approach the poles. Cytokinesis (cell division) usually begins.

Metaphase
Kinetochore microtubules orient duplicated chromosomes on the metaphase plate.

Spindle

Early anaphase
The two centromeres of each pair of sister chromatids separated and the resuting daughter chromosomes begin migration to opposite poles.

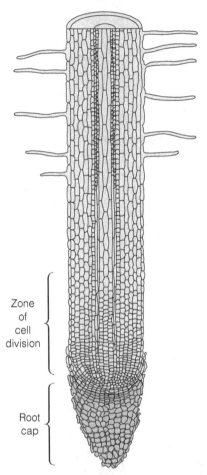

Figure 3.4.
Longitudinal section through a root tip. Cells are dividing in the zone of cell division just behind the root cap.

Reprinted from *Investigating Biology Lab Manual*, Seventh Edition, by Jane B. Reece, et.al. (2011), Benjamin Cummings, a Pearson Education Company.

Procedure:

1. Examine a prepared slide of a longitudinal section through an onion root tip using low power on the compound microscope.

2. Locate the region most likely to have dividing cells, just behind the root cap (Figure 3.4).

    At the tip of the root is a root cap that protects the tender root tip as it grows through the soil. Just behind the root cap is the **zone of cell division.** Notice that rows of cells extend upward from this zone. As cells divide in the zone of cell division, the root tip is pushed farther into the soil. Cells produced by division begin to mature, elongating and differentiating into specialized cells, such as those that conduct water and nutrients throughout the plant.

3. Focus on the zone of cell division. Then switch to the intermediate power, focus, and switch to high power.

4. Survey the zone of cell division and locate stages of the cell cycle: interphase, prophase, prometaphase, metaphase, anaphase, telophase, and cytokinesis.

5. As you find a dividing cell, speculate about its stage of division, read the following descriptions given of each stage to verify that your guess is correct, and, if necessary, confirm your conclusion with the instructor.

6. Draw the cell in the appropriate boxes provided. Label nucleus, nucleolus, chromosome, chromatin, mitotic spindle, and cell plate when appropriate.

Interphase (G_1, S, G_2)

Nuclear material is surrounded by a nuclear envelope. Dark-staining bodies, nucleoli, are visible. Chromosomes appear only as dark granules within the nucleus. Collectively, the chromosome mass is called *chromatin.* The chromosomes are not individually distinguishable because they are uncoiled into long, thin strands. Chromosomes are replicated during this phase.

Prophase

Chromosomes begin to coil and become distinguishable thin, threadlike structures, widely dispersed in the nucleus during prophase. Although there are no centrioles in plant cells, a spindle begins to form. Nucleoli begin to disappear. The nuclear envelope is still intact.

Prometaphase

By prometaphase, the chromosomes are thick and short. Each chromosome is duplicated consisting of two chromatids held together by a centromere. The nuclear membrane and nucleoli break down in prometaphase. Chromosomes move toward the equator.

Metaphase

Metaphase begins when the centromeres of the chromosomes lie on the equator of the cell. The arms of the chromatids extend randomly in all directions. A spindle may be apparent. Spindle fibers are attached to kinetochores at the centromere region and extend to the poles of the cell. As metaphase ends and anaphase begins, the centromeres split.

Anaphase

The splitting of centromeres marks the beginning of anaphase. Each former chromatid is now a new single chromosome. These chromosomes are drawn apart toward opposite poles of the cell. Anaphase ends when the migrating chromosomes reach their respective poles.

Telophase and Cytokinesis

Chromosomes have now reached the poles. The nuclear envelope re-forms around each compact mass of chromosomes. Nucleoli reappear. Chromosomes begin to uncoil and become indistinct. Cytokinesis is accomplished by the formation of a cell plate that begins in the center of the equatorial plane and grows outward to the cell wall.

ACTIVITY 3.2.2
Observing Mitosis and Cytokinesis in Animal Cells

Introduction

The most convenient source of actively dividing cells in animals is the early embryo, where cells are large and divide rapidly with a short interphase. In blastulas (an early embryonic stage), a large percentage of cells will be dividing at any given time. By examining cross sections of whitefish blastulas, you should be able to locate many dividing cells in various stages of mitosis and cytokinesis.

Materials:

1. Prepared slides of whitefish blastula sections
2. Compound microscope

Procedure

1. Examine a prepared slide of whitefish blastula cross sections. Find a blastula section on the lowest power, focus, switch to intermediate power, focus, and switch to high power.
2. As you locate a dividing cell, identify the stage of mitosis. *Be able to recognize all stages of mitosis in these cells.*
3. Identify the following in several cells:

   nucleus, **nuclear envelope**, and **nucleolus**

   chromosomes

   mitotic spindle

   asters—an array of microtubules surrounding each centriole pair at the poles of the spindle

   centrioles—small dots seen at the poles around which the microtubules of the spindle and asters appear to radiate

   cleavage furrow
4. Sketch and make notes regarding the various stages of mitosis that you observed in the whitefish blatula slides using the blank page provide in your lab manual.

Reprinted from Investigating Biology Lab Manual, Seventh Edition, by Jane B. Reece, et.al. (2011), Benjamin Cummings, a Pearson Education Company.

ACTIVITY 3.2.3
Observing Human Chromosomes

Introduction

Cytogeneticists examining dividing cells of humans can frequently detect chromosome abnormalities that lead to severe mental retardation. To examine human chromosomes, leukocytes are isolated from a small sample of the patient's blood and cultured in a medium that inhibits spindle formation during mitosis. As cells begin mitosis, chromosomes condense and become distinct, but in the absence of a spindle they cannot move to the poles in anaphase. You will observe a slide in which many cells have chromosomes condensed as in prometaphase or metaphase, but they are not aligned on a spindle equator.

Materials:

1. Slides of human leukocytes (on demonstration at the side bench)

Procedure

1. Attempt to count the chromosomes in one cell in the field of view. Normally, humans have 46 chromosomes. Persons with trisomy 21 (three copies of chromosome 21), or Down syndrome, have 47 chromosomes. Are the cells on this slide from a person with a normal chromosome number?

2. Notice that each chromosome is duplicated, being made up of two sister chromatids held together by a single centromere. In very high magnifications, bands can be seen on the chromosomes. Abnormalities in banding patterns can also be an indication of severe mental retardation.

ACTIVITY 3.3

Analysis of Meiosis in Plant and Animal Cells (~20 minutes)

THIS ACTIVITY IS DONE INDIVIDUALLY

In this activity you will observe the stages of meiosis in lily anthers and grasshopper testes. An overview of meiosis can be seen in Figure 3.5.

Figure 3.5

The stages of meiosis in an animal cell.

Reprinted from iGenetics: A Molecular Approach, Third Edition, by Peter J. Russell (2010), Benjamin Cummings, a Pearson Education Company

Early prophase I

Chromosomes, already duplicated, become visible. Centriole pairs begin separation and a spindle forms between them.

Middle prophase I

Homologous chromosomes shorten and thicken. The chromosomes synapse and crossing-over occurs.

Late prophase I/Prometaphase I

Results of crossing-over become visible as chiasmata. Nuclear envelope breaks down. Meiotic spindle enters the former nuclear area. Kinetochore microtubules attach to the chromosomes.

Metaphase I

Kinetochore microtubules align each chromosome pair (the tetrads) on the metaphase plate.

Anaphase I

Chromosomes in each tetrad separate and begin migrating toward opposite poles.

Telophase I

Chromosomes (each with two sister chromatids) complete migration to the poles and new nuclear envelopes may form. (Other sorting patterns are possible.)

Cytokinesis

In most species, cytokinesis occurs to produce two cells. Chromosomes do not replicate before meiosis II.

Prophase II

Metaphase II

Anaphase II

Telophase II

4 gametes

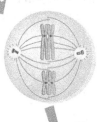
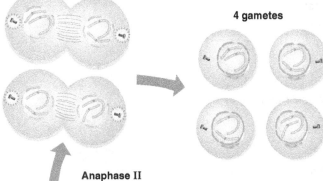

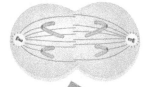

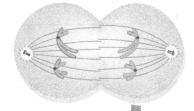
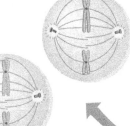

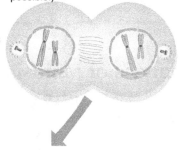
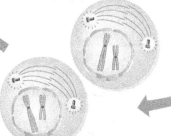

ACTIVITY 3.3.1
Meiosis in Plant Cells

Description:

In the lily, gametes are produced via meiosis in the male structures, called anthers, and the female ovules.

Materials:

1. Prepared lily anther section slides (on demonstration at the side bench)

Procedure:

1. Examine the lily anther slides on demonstration and identify the stages of meiosis I, meiosis II, and cytokinesis (see Figure 3.5 for an overview of all of the stages).

2. Sketch and make notes regarding the various stages of meiosis that you observed in the lily anther slides using the blank page provided in your lab manual.

ACTIVITY 3.3.2
Meiosis in Animal Cells

Description:

In the grasshopper (an insect), gametes are produced via meiosis in the male testes (producing sperm) and in the female ovaries (producing eggs).

Materials:

1. Prepared grasshopper testis slides
2. Compound microscope

Procedure:

1. Examine the grasshopper testis slides at your bench and identify the stages of meiosis I, meiosis II, and cytokinesis (see Figure 3.5 for an overview of all of the stages). Most stages should be observable on a single slide.
2. Sketch and make notes regarding the various stages of meiosis that you observed in the grasshopper testis slide using the blank page provided in your lab manual.

ACTIVITY 3.4

Identification of Unknowns and Completion of Lab Worksheet
(~30 Minutes)

THIS ACTIVITY IS DONE IN GROUPS OF 4.

Description:

In this activity you will examine several colour plates (pictures) showing the various stages of mitosis and meiosis from the plants and animals that you have already seen in Activities 3.2 and 3.3. In your groups, you will determine which stage and organism is seen in each plate.

Materials:

Set of unknowns

Procedure:

1. You will be given a set of unknowns by your TA. Record the numbers of the unknowns (found on the back of each picture) in the appropriate table in your Lab 3 Worksheet.
2. Identify the cell type (i.e., plant or animal), and stage of mitosis or meiosis for each unknown.
3. Document the evidence you observe that indicates the stage of mitosis or meiosis in the appropriate column of the worksheet table.
4. Draw an image of the cell you see in the appropriate column of the worksheet table.
5. Complete the rest of your Lab 3 worksheet.

Check Your Understanding:
Reviewing Your Knowledge

1. Define the following terms and use each in a meaningful sentence. Give examples when appropriate.

   mitosis, meiosis, cytokinesis, chromosome, chromatin, centromere, centriole, centrosome, kinetochore, spindle, aster, homologous chromosome, synaptonemal complex, synapsis, tetrad, chiasma, sister chromatid, nucleolus, cell plate, cleavage furrow, diploid, haploid, crossing over, mycelium, perithecium, ascus

2. Describe the activity of chromosomes in each stage of mitosis.
3. In the photomicrograph of dividing root cells at right, identify interphase and the following phases of mitosis: prophase, metaphase, anaphase, telophase, and cytokinesis.
4. Describe the activity of chromosomes in each stage of meiosis I and meiosis II.

5. Observe the drawing of several phases of meiosis below.

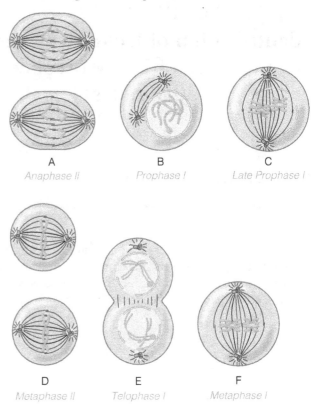

a. Using the designated letters, list the phases of meiosis in sequence.
b. Label each stage (include I or II).
c. At what stage would crossing over occur?
d. What is the diploid number for this organism?

6. Mitosis is important as organisms, both animals and plants, increase in size and grow new tissues and organs. Unlike animals, plants continue to grow throughout their life. Where would you expect mitosis to be most common in the body of a mature plant?

7. What role would mitosis play in the body of an adult animal?

8. What advantage does the process of crossing over bring to reproduction?

9. Why would the method of cytokinesis in animal cells not work in plant cells?

Apply What You Know:

1. You have probably heard that the liver of an adult human can "regenerate itself." How is the process of regeneration related to mitosis? Why is it possible to have a living donor for a transplanted liver?

2. Identical twins Jan and Fran were very close sisters. So, when Jan died suddenly, Fran moved in to help take care of Jan's daughter (her niece), Millie. Some time later Fran married her brother-in-law and became Millie's stepmother. When Fran announced that she was pregnant, poor Millie became confused and curious. "So," Millie asked, "who is this baby? Will she be my twin? Will she be my sister, my stepsister, my cousin?" Can you answer her questions? What is the genetic relationship between Millie and the baby? What processes are involved in the formation of gametes and how do they affect genetic variation?

3. Two natural plant products, vinblastine from the rosy periwinkle and paclitaxel (taxol) from the Pacific yew, have been used successfully in the treatment of a wide range of cancers. These chemicals work by interfering with mitosis but by different methods. Vinblastine inhibits mitosis by preventing the assembly of the spindle. Paclitaxel promotes microtubule synthesis and binds to the microtubules preventing the de-polymerization (disassembly) of the spindle during mitosis. Based on your knowledge of mitosis, at what phase do you expect cell division to be interrupted by each of these cancer-fighting compounds? Explain your answer based on the activities occurring at the mitotic stage.

References:

Becker, W. M., L. Kleinsmith, J. Hardin and G. Bertoni. *The World of the Cell,* 7th ed. Redwood City, CA: Benjamin Cummings, 2003 to 2009.

Bold, H. C., C. J. Alexopoulos, and T. Delevoryas. *Morphology of Plants and Fungi.* New York: Harper & Row, 1980.

Costello, M. and K. Kellmel. "Medical Attributes of *Taxus brevifolia*—The Pacific Yew" [online] available at http://wilkesl.wilkes.edu/~kklemow/Taxus.html, 2003.

Holden, C. "A Long-lost Relative," *Science,* 2007, vol. 316, p. 669.

Olive, L. S. "Genetics of *Sordaria fimicola.* I. Ascospore color mutants." *American Journal of Botany,* 1956, vol. 43, p. 97.

Snyder, Lucy. "Pharmacology of Vinblastine, Vincristine Vindesine and Vinorelbine." *Cyberbotanica.* [online] available at http://biotech.icmb.utexas.edu/botany/vvv.html, 2004.

UTM Biology Faculty Profile:

Dr. Bryan Stewart studies the molecular mechanisms of neuronal function and development using electrophysiology, biochemistry, electron microscopy and imaging techniques.

Recent Publications:

Kisiel, M., Majumdar, D., Campbell, S., & Stewart, B. A. 2011. Myosin VI contributes to synaptic transmission and development at the *Drosophila* neuromuscular junction. *BMC Neuroscience,* 12: 65.

Seabrooke, S., Qiu, X., & Stewart, B. A. 2010. Nonmuscle myosin II helps regulate synaptic vesicle mobility at the *Drosophila* neuromuscular junction. *BMC Neuroscience,* 11:37.

Seabrooke, S., & Stewart, B. A. 2011. Synaptic transmission and plasticity are modulated by nonmuscle myosin II at the neuromuscular junction of *Drosophila. Journal of Neurophysiology,* 105(5): 1966-1976.

For more information about Dr. Stewart's lab, research interest and publications, visit his website at:http://www.utm.utoronto.ca/~bstewart/

Reprinted from *Investigating Biology Lab Manual,* Seventh Edition, by Jane B. Reece, et.al. (2011), Benjamin Cummings, a Pearson Education Company.

BIO152 Laboratory 4
Natural Selection

The lab 4 assignment involves the completion of an individual assignment (assignment details and templates are found via the 'Labs' link on the course Blackboard site). Your assignment is due at the beginning of Lab 5 (i.e., next week).

Overview

In this laboratory exercise you will examine various traits in isopods (Class Crustacea, Order Isopoda) and determine whether or not these traits confer a survival advantage when the isopods are subjected to simulated predation.

Preparation

1. Read through the entire lab and associated assignment instructions.
2. Review textbook chapters 24 & 25.
3. BRING A **CALCULATOR** TO LAB!

Laboratory Objectives

After completing this laboratory exercise, you should be able to:
1. Define natural selection
2. Understand the relationship between variation and selection
3. Be able to collect, organize, and analyze a large amount of data
4. Answer the following question:

What characteristics do you hypothesize will increase survival in isopods?

Background Information

Mechanisms of evolutionary change cause changes in the frequency of genes in populations. In addition to genetic drift, mutation and migration (gene flow), **natural selection** is one of the key mechanisms of evolutionary change. Natural selection is defined as the differential survival and reproduction of organisms that exhibit differences in heritable traits. As such, organisms that are better adapted to the environment will increase in frequency relative to those that are less suited to their environment. So, as long as there is variation in traits in a population of organisms, there is differential reproduction as a result of selection pressures. These beneficial heritable traits will then be passed on to subsequent generations and the trait will become more common in the population.

Darwin proposed that the net effect of the forms of selection acting on a population of organisms could result in the evolution of new species. For example, Darwin studied the finches of the Galapagos Islands and found that the shape and size of their beaks varied considerably. This variation seems to have evolved in response to the variation in seeds that the finches eat (Grant, 1986).

This variation in the phenotypic state of the finches can be visualized in a **frequency distribution**. Frequency is how often something occurs, so a frequency distribution is a graphical representation of how many times something occurs within a group of categories or ranges. For example, say you had a random sample of birds and you sorted and counted the birds according to beak morphology (Table 4.1). You then plot this data graphically with the variable (in this case beak morphology) on the x-axis and the frequency (in this case the number of birds with each beak morphology) on the y-axis (Figure 4.1). This frequency distribution provides the following information: the range of phenotypic states (or the range of different beak morphologies), the frequency of individuals with each phenotypic state, as well as where the mean would be within the population (according to the shape of the curve), and finally the amount of variation (which is indicated by the breadth of the distribution).

Table 4.1
Frequency of birds with each beak morphological adaptation.

Beak Morphology	# of birds within the category
Long, pointed	3
short, broad	7
downward curve	10
scissor	5
rounded	1

A way of characterizing a selection event involves measuring the intensity of a selection pressure. Selection intensity is the difference between the mean value of a phenotypic trait after selection and the mean of the phenotypic trait of the total (original) population.

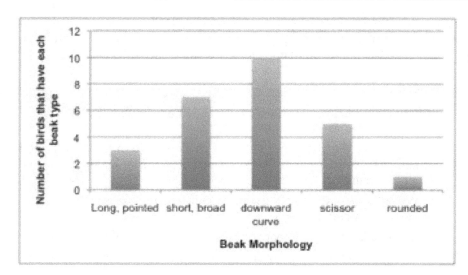

Figure 4.1
Frequency distribution of bird beak morphology

ACTIVITY 4.1
Simulation of Predation of Isopods and Measurement of Potentially Adaptive Traits

---

Description:

The organism that you will be studying in lab today is the terrestrial isopod, also called the sowbug, pill bug, or potato bug. Isopods are small crustaceans that have 7 pairs of legs and breathe with gill-like structures located at the posterior end of the body. Because isopods require gills to breath, they must inhabit wet or moist environments such as marine, freshwater and moist terrestrial environments (such as under leaf litter and logs). Isopods are omnivores or scavengers, which feed on dead or decaying plants and animals. Predators of isopods are varied and include: ants, spiders, toads, frogs, some birds, beetles, and even other isopods. Isopods vary in physical characteristics such as size, running speed, the ability to roll into a ball and coloration. Some of these characteristics may be adaptations to eluding predators.

In this lab activity, you will work in groups of four students to simulate predation on isopods. You will utilize a spoon to represent the predator. You will then measure some potentially adaptive traits (size and speed). In your assignment, you will further analyze your data to determine if the measured traits are adaptive with respect to predator avoidance.

Materials:

1. Isopods
2. Spoon
3. Stopwatch
4. Predation arena with aluminum foil that acts as a refuge from predation

5. 2 plastic containers with lids: label survivors or victims
6. Other materials: damp paper towel, holding containers for the isopods, race track lined with damp cloth, 24-well plates, ruler

Procedure:

(Adapted from: http://www.ableweb.org/volumes/vol-19/15-berkelhamer.pdf)

Part 1: Simulated Predation

1. One person from the group collects 15 isopods from the main isopod tank and places them in the holding container. *Isopods are fragile and must be handled very gently*.
2. While the isopods are being collected, the other group members assemble the observation arena:
   a. Put a layer of damp paper towels on the bottom of the platter.
   b. Drape aluminum foil over ¼ of the platter to act as cover and refuge for the isopods
   c. Put paper cover over the top of the holding container of isopods and carefully invert the container and place it in the centre of the observation arena. Leave the isopods for a couple of minutes to acclimate to the environment before releasing them into the area.
3. Choose one group member to act as the predator. The predator will now simulate predation by using the spoon to pick up isopods for **30 seconds**. *Please try not to injure the isopods during the predation process*.
   a. Place the **captured isopods** in the plastic container labeled **victims**.
   b. After the predation trial is over one group member transfers the **remaining isopods from the arena** to the plastic container labeled **survivors**.

Part 2: Measurement of Isopod Speed and Size

1. Now that you have simulated predation and have your victims and survivors in their respective containers, now you need to measure their physical traits. One group member is responsible for transferring each isopod from its victim or survivor container to clearly numbered well in a 24-well plate. This group member must record the survivor and victim IDs in Table 4.2. Make sure to randomize the numbering and do not tell the other group members whether a given isopod is a victim or survivor. Please only divulge this information to the rest of the group once all of the traits have been measured.
2. Once each isopod has been transferred to its own numbered well in the plate, measurement of the traits can begin. Complete the measurement of the following traits.
   a. Measure isopod length
      i. While the isopod is in the well, measure the total length of the isopod using a ruler and a hand lens if necessary. Record the length in millimeters in Table 4.2.
   b. Measure sprint speed
      a Place a strip of moist cloth on the bottom of a plastic race track.
         i. One person will release an isopod at one end of the track
         ii. Allow the isopod about 5 seconds to adjust to the new environment
         iii. The second person should then start the timer and time for 10 seconds

iv. Record the time and distance the isopod travels down the track in Table 4.2. Be very careful that you are recording the results for the right isopod so make sure to confirm the well number with the isopod number in the chart.

v. When the isopod has completed this speed test, place it back into holding container 1 and not back into the 24-well plate.

vi. Convert the time and distance to speed by dividing the distance by the time. Record this information in Table 4.2.

3. After all measurements are completed on all of the isopods for this first predation trial repeat Parts 1 and 2 and do a second predation trial.

4. At the end of the second predation trial place the isopods back into the large holding tank. Please do not put any isopods that may have died back into the holding tank. Please put deceased isopods into the isopod discard container

Table 4.2: Isopod trait measurement

Victim (V) Survivor (S)	Isopod number	Distance (cm) in 10 seconds	Calculate the Speed (cm/s)	Body length (mm)	
					First predation trial
					Second predation trial

Check Your Understanding:

1. Do species only evolve by natural selection?
2. What factors are necessary for natural selection?
3. Do individual organisms evolve? Explain.
4. Why did you have to wait a couple of minutes for the isopods to get used to the arena before you started the predation trial?
5. What morphological feature of an isopod predator might the spoon be simulating?
6. Why is damp paper towel being used throughout the laboratory exercises?
7. Why is it important not to tell other group members whether a particular isopod is a victim or survivor?
8. Do you think that the isopods you collected were a random sample of those living in the tank, or those living in the wild? Do you think you may have unconsciously selected for certain traits when you simulated the predation? If so, what was the trait you think you may have selected for?
9. How much variation should you expect to see in each of the traits that you observed and measured?
10. Why might some traits be more variable than others?
11. Was there a difference between the results of the first predation trial and second predation trial? What factors could account for the differences you may have observed?

Apply What You Know:

Consider the case of the red-bellied Pacu. This fish lives in Papua New Guinea and is a cousin of the piranha. The Pacu's diet consists of mainly plants, but also nuts, and some insects. In more recent years this fish has started to eat more and more fish and has even been known to bite humans. Why might the Pacu change its diet so drastically from eating mainly plant material to eating mainly fish? What adaptations might the Pacu have to be able to make this switch?

Why Is This Important?

Natural selection is a powerful process and helps us explain the overwhelming array of adaptations seen in nature. The overall importance of natural selection is seen in the potential to produce new species. The Earth is very diverse; not only in the number of species of plants, animals, etc., but also in the diverse array of genes within these species and the varied environments and ecosystems that organisms inhabit. Biodiversity is extremely important but biodiversity losses are continuing, which could result in more species extinctions.

Additional Investigations and Applications:

Current investigations in evolutionary biology are trying to determine how evolution occurs. Some of the research questions currently being investigated are:

- The mechanics of evolution with respect to development—since the genes that determine features are subject to natural and sexual selection, what is the role of these two processes in development?

- How does evolution progress—is it a slow and steady process or does it happen abruptly between long periods of quiescence?

- Why is there asymmetry in the diversity within groups of organisms? For instance, some clades have numerous species while others have very few.

- What processes have affected human evolution?

Additional Resources:

Grant, P. R. 1986. Ecology and Evolution of Darwin's Finches. Princeton University Press, New Jersey, 458 pages.

UTM Biology Faculty Profile:

Sampling sea grass (Spartina) on Sapelo Island, Univ. of Georgia Marine Research Station as part of a study on farming of fungi in plants by snails - and the decline of sea grass along the Atlantic coast of North America. (Picture Courtesy of Prof. Kohn)

Dr. Linda Kohn studies fungal systematics and evolution. Current research in the Kohn lab focuses on mechanisms of speciation in fungi, mechanisms of trophic preference in pathogenic fungi and population and community dynamics of fungi in plants.

Recent Publications:

- Andrew, M., Barua, R., Short, S. M., & Kohn, L. M. 2012. Evidence for a common toolbox based on necrotrophy in a fungal lineage spanning necrotrophs, biotrophs, endophytes, host generalists and specialists. *PLoS ONE*, 7(1): e29943.

- Parreiras, L. S., Kohn, L. M., & Anderson, J. B. 2011. Cellular effects and epistasis among three determinants of adaptation in experimental populations of *Saccharomyces cerevisiae*. *Eukaryotic Cell*, 10(10): 1348-1356.

- Anderson, J.B., Funt, J., Thompson D.A., Prabhu, S., Socha, A., Sirjusingh, C., Dettman, J.R., Parreiras, L., Guttman D.S., Regev, A., Kohn, L.M. 2010. Determinants of divergent adaptation and Dobzhansky-Muller interaction in experimental yeast populations. *Current Biology*, 20(15): 1383-1388.

- Saunders, M., Glenn, A. E., & Kohn, L. M. 2010. Exploring the evolutionary ecology of fungal endophytes in agricultural systems: Using functional traits to reveal mechanisms in community processes. *Evolutionary Applications*: 3(5-6): 525-537.

For more information about Dr. Kohn's lab, research interests and publications, visit her website at:
http://erin.utoronto.ca/~kohnmank/index.htm

BIO152 Laboratory 5
Patterns of Inheritance

The lab 5 assignment involves the completion of a group worksheet (found via the 'Labs' link on the course Blackboard site). The worksheet is due at the end of your lab (i.e., BEFORE you leave).

Overview

In this lab exercise, you will examine and analyze the frequency of two different genetic traits: (1) The ability to taste PTC (autosomal dominant) and (2) red-green colour blindness (X-linked recessive).

Preparation

1. Read through the entire lab and associated worksheet(s).
2. Review Appendix 3, 4, and 5 (guides to basic genetics problem solving, including Hardy-Weinberg population genetics and pedigree analysis).
3. Review Chapters 13 and 25 of your textbook.
4. BRING **A CALCULATOR** TO LAB!

Laboratory Objectives

After completing this laboratory exercise, you should be able to:

1. Understand the concept of Hardy-Weinberg equilibrium and be able to calculate allele and genotype frequencies for autosomal and sex-linked traits using Hardy-Weinberg equations.
2. Consider why allele and genotype frequencies may not be in Hardy-Weinberg equilibrium.
3. Consider both the pattern of inheritance and the possible evolutionary significance of certain human traits.
4. Practice solving genetics problems and pedigree analysis.

Background Information

Though Mendel and others asked the question of why offspring resemble their parents, the reverse question is also important—why do even closely related individuals vary considerably in appearance and behaviour? These differences exist because all individuals inherit unique combinations of genes from their parents. Unique combinations of genes are a direct result of meiosis acting on the shuffling of different alleles.

The frequencies of different alleles in a population may vary depending on the effect of four evolutionary processes: Natural selection, genetic drift, gene flow, and mutation. Natural selection may increase the frequency of alleles that increase survival and/or the ability to reproduce. Genetic drift results in random changes in allele frequencies, usually in small populations. Gene flow results in allele frequency changes when there is migration between populations; this can result in the introduction of new alleles or the loss of existing alleles. Mutations introduce new alleles into a population thus changing the allele frequencies. In order to determine if any of these evolutionary processes are acting on a particular trait, we can compare observed allele and genotype frequencies to those predicted by the Hardy-Weinberg model.

The Hardy-Weinberg model of genetic equilibrium proposes specific conditions where **NO** evolution occurs in a population. The five assumptions/conditions of the Hardy-Weinberg model are:

1. A specific allele does not confer a selective (or survival) advantage over another.
2. Mating is random (no sexual selection).
3. The population is extremely large so that there is no genetic drift of other random changes in allele frequencies.
4. There is no migration and therefore no gene flow.
5. There is no mutation.

If the conditions of the Hardy-Weinberg model are satisfied, allele frequencies will not change from generation to generation (see Figure 5.1).

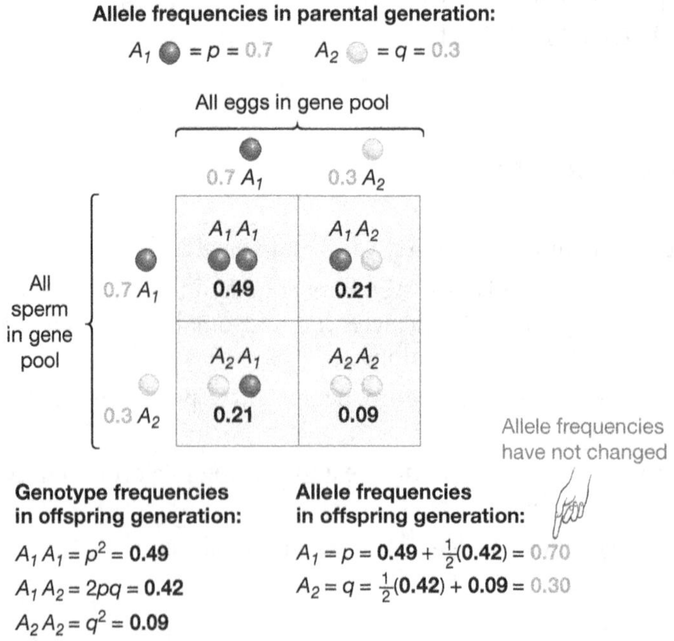

Figure 5.1

A Punnett Square Illustrates the Hardy-Weinberg Principle. Reprinted from *Biological Science Canadian Edition,* by Scott Freeman, et.al (2011), Pearson Canada Inc. a Pearson Education Company.

Allele frequencies in parental generation:

A_1 ● $= p = 0.7$ A_2 ○ $= q = 0.3$

All eggs in gene pool

	$0.7\ A_1$	$0.3\ A_2$
$0.7\ A_1$	A_1A_1 **0.49**	A_1A_2 **0.21**
$0.3\ A_2$	A_2A_1 **0.21**	A_2A_2 **0.09**

All sperm in gene pool

Allele frequencies have not changed

Genotype frequencies in offspring generation:

$A_1A_1 = p^2 = \mathbf{0.49}$

$A_1A_2 = 2pq = \mathbf{0.42}$

$A_2A_2 = q^2 = \mathbf{0.09}$

Allele frequencies in offspring generation:

$A_1 = p = 0.49 + \frac{1}{2}(0.42) = 0.70$

$A_2 = q = \frac{1}{2}(0.42) + 0.09 = 0.30$

If dealing with two alleles of an autosomal gene, the sum of the allele frequencies is equal to one ($p + q = 1$). Note that the sum of the genotype frequencies is also one ($p2 + 2pq + q^2 = 1$). Allele frequencies are calculated as follows:

1) For two alleles (*A* and *a*) of an autosomal gene:

$$p = f(A) = \frac{2(\text{number of } AA \text{ individuals}) + (\text{number of } Aa \text{ individuals})}{2(\text{total number of individuals})}$$

$$q = f(a) = \frac{2(\text{number of } aa \text{ individuals}) + (\text{number of } Aa \text{ individuals})}{2(\text{total number of individuals})}$$

2) For two alleles (X^A and X^a) of an X-linked gene:

$$p = f(X^A) = \frac{2(\text{number of } X^AX^A \text{ females}) + (\text{number of } X^AX^a \text{ females}) + (\text{number of } X^AY \text{ males})}{2(\text{number of females}) + (\text{number of males})}$$

$$q = f(X^a) = \frac{2(\text{number of } X^aX^a \text{ females}) + (\text{number of } X^AX^a \text{ females}) + (\text{number of } X^aY \text{ males})}{2(\text{number of females}) + (\text{number of males})}$$

If the observed allele and/or genotype frequencies differ significantly from the expected frequencies of the Hardy-Weinberg model, the population is evolving (with respect to the particular trait that is being examined).

ACTIVITY 5.1
Taste Bud (Fungiform Papillae) Count and PTC Taste Threshold.

Description:
Phenylthiocarbamide (PTC, or phenylthiourea) is a chemical compound that can be extremely bitter or almost completely tasteless depending on the genetic make-up of the tester. You may already have some idea of your ability to taste PTC as PTC-related compounds are found in many cruciferous vegetables including broccoli, cabbage, cauliflower, bok choy, and other leafy green vegetables. While PTC-related compounds are found in many vegetables that are considered very healthy for you, it has also been hypothesized that the ability to taste PTC may be correlated to the ability to taste, and thus avoid the ingestion of, toxic compounds.

The ability to taste PTC has been correlated to the number of taste-buds (fungiform papillae) on a person's tongue (see Figure 5.2). The more papillae you have, the more taste-buds you have and the more sensitive you are to different tastes (including PTC).

PTC tasting is an example of an incompletely dominant genetic trait. **Super-tasters** are homozygous dominant, **tasters** are heterozygous and **non-tasters** are homozygous recessive. The frequency of the PTC non-taster allele (i.e., the recessive allele) is ~50% in the world-wide population, but this can vary between different populations.

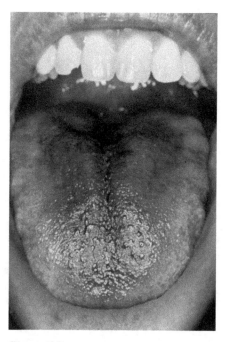

Figure 5.2

Comparison of the number of papillae in various types of tasters. The pink dots are fungiform papillae; they don't take up the food colouring. These papillae are the tiny bumps on your tongue that house your taste buds. The more papillae you have, the more taste buds you have and the more sensitve to taste you are. On average, non-tasters have fewer than 15 papillae in that area, while supertasters have over 30. Courtesy of John T. Carbone/Getty Imagesm Inc.

In this lab activity you will: (1) count your taste buds and determine your PTC taste threshold, (2) determine if the number of taste-buds is correlated to the ability to taste PTC (based on class data), and (3) determine if your class is in Hardy-Weinberg equilibrium with respect to this trait.

Materials:

Taste-bud Counting

1. Blue food colouring
2. Sterile cotton buds (Q-tips)
3. Reinforcement rings
4. Magnifying glass

PTC Taste Threshold

1. Series of dilutions of PTC (Table 5.1)
2. Sterile cotton buds (Q-tips)

Table 5.1: PTC solutions and corresponding tube labels.

Tube #	Parts of stock (860 mg/l) diluted with tap water
0	Control
1	1 in 256
2	1 in 128
3	1 in 64
4	1 in 32
5	1 in 16
6	1 in 8
7	1 in 4
8	1 in 2

Procedure:

Taste-bud Counting
(Adapted from:
http://www.bbc.co.uk/science/humanbody/body/articles/senses/tongue_experiment.shtml)

1. Using a cotton Q-tip, swab some blue food colouring onto the tip of your tongue.
2. Place a reinforcement ring on your tongue.
3. Your partner will use a magnifying glass to count the pink dots within the reinforcement ring.
4. Record the number of papillae on your tongue: _____.
5. Record your result in the class data table on the chalkboard. Once all students have recorded their data on the chalkboard, copy down the class data and use it to complete the Lab 5 worksheet.

PTC Taste Threshold
(Adapted from: http://learn.genetics.utah.edu)
You will be testing a series of numbered solutions **starting with the water (Tube 0) and going from the most dilute to the most concentrated solution (i.e., Tube 0 to Tube 8) using a clean Q-tip for each tube**.

1. Use a **CLEAN** Q-tip for each phase of the testing procedure. Dip the Q-tip into Tube 0, and then touch the Q-tip to your tongue. Discard the Q-tip in the waste bucket provided.
2. Repeat the above procedure for the remaining tubes. Stop once you are able to taste PTC, and record your threshold on the class data table posted on the chalkboard. The taste threshold is the number of the solution that you can first taste something bitter/sour.
3. Record your PTC threshold: Tube # _____.
4. Record your result in the class data table on the chalkboard. Once all students have recorded their data on the chalkboard, copy down the class data and use it to complete the Lab 5 worksheet.

ACTIVITY 5.2
Red-Green Colour Blindness

Description:

Red-green 'colour blindness' is inherited as an X-linked recessive trait. In the general population, ~8% of males and ~0.5% of females are colour blind. During lab you will be screened for this trait. Your TA will test one student from each lab bench to see if they are colour blind. That student will then proceed to test the other students at their lab bench.

Materials:

1. Red-green colour blindness test plates.

Procedure:

1. Choose one student from your bench to be the first one tested for red-green colour blindness.
2. Your TA will then test this student and teach them how to administer the test to the other lab bench members.
3. The student will then test the other students at their bench.
4. Record your result in the class data table on the chalkboard. Once all students have recorded their data on the chalkboard, copy down the class data and use it to complete the Lab 5 worksheet.

Check Your Understanding:

1. What is the pattern of inheritance for the ability to taste PTC?
2. If you really hate eating cruciferous vegetables (i.e., you find them way too bitter), do you think that your PTC taste threshold would be low or high?
3. Explain how the ability to taste PTC might be considered adaptive (advantageous)?
4. Explain how the ability to taste PTC might be considered maladaptive (disadvantageous)?
5. Based on what you know about the ability to taste PTC, do you expect the frequency of the 'taster' allele in the population to be low or high?
6. Do you expect people with more taste buds per unit area to have a lower taste threshold for PTC? Why?
7. What is the pattern of inheritance for red-green colour blindness? Why are males affected more than females?
8. If red-green colour blindness is not adaptive, why hasn't the allele been bred out of the population?
9. Have we collected enough data in lab to tell if these two traits (PTC tasting and colour blindness) are evolving? Explain.

Apply What You Know:

1. A woman has a widow's peak, but she does not know her genotype. She marries a man who has a straight hairline and they have 13 children.

Nine have widow's peaks and four have straight hairlines. What are the genotypes of the parents? What are the genotypes of the children? Explain how you arrived at your answers.

2. A couple who both have the ability to roll their tongues have a son who is also a tongue-roller. The son is very curious as to whether he is homozygous or heterozygous for the tongue-rolling trait. How would he go about finding out?

3. You are a genetic counselor, and a man and woman come to you to discuss their family history and assess their risk of having a child affected with Tay-Sachs or hemophilia A. The woman's maternal grandfather had hemophilia A. No other people in her family are known to have had hemophilia. The man's paternal grandfather's brother had Tay-Sachs, and the woman's paternal uncle had Tay-Sachs. No other people in the family are known to have had Tay-Sachs. Assume that these mutations are very rare in this population. Tay-Sachs is an autosomal recessive disorder, and hemophilia A is an x-linked recessive disorder. Based on this information, what is the probability that the man and woman would have a child with Tay-Sachs? What is the probability that the man and woman would have a child that is a carrier for Tay-Sachs? What is the probability that the man and the woman would have a boy with hemophilia A? What is the probability that the man and woman would have a girl that is a carrier for hemophilia A?

Why Is This Important?

*   Mendelian principles apply to all eukaryotes. Study of the inheritance of genetic traits in humans is more difficult because controlled crosses cannot be done within ethical bounds. Instead, human geneticists examine genetic traits by pedigree analysis—that is, by following the occurrence of a trait in family trees in which the trait is segregating.
*   Population genetics seeks to understand the genetic basis of evolutionary change by determining the mechanisms underlying the observed patterns of genetic variation within and among populations in nature. This field of study includes both empirical and theoretical approaches to testing hypotheses about the evolutionary processes that change gene frequencies.
*   Principles of population genetics can inform us about our genetic heritage and can also be applied to the management of rare and endangered species. Genetic diversity is best maintained by establishing a population with adequate founders, expanding the population rapidly, avoiding inbreeding.

Reprinted from *iGenetics: A Molecular Approach*, Third Edition, by Peter J. Russell (2010), Benjamin Cummings, a Pearson Education Company.

Additional Investigations and Applications:

Molecular geneticists interested in the evolutionary history of the human race have concentrated their research on samples of DNA from women representing all races and continents. Why might the DNA of women – and not men – be of interest?

Additional Resources:

To help you visualize what you will be doing in lab, look at the following:
http://learn.genetics.utah.edu/CONTENT/BEGIN/TRAITS/PTC/

References:

Guo, S. W. & Reed, D.R. 2001. The genetics of phenylthiocarbamide perception. *Annals of Human Biology,* **28**(2): 111-142.

Klug, W.S., M.R. Cummings, C. Spencer, and M.A. Palladino. *Essentials of Genetics,* 7th ed. San Francisco, CA: Benjamin Cummings, 2010.

Wooding, S., Kim, S.K., Bamshad, M.J., et al. 2004. Natural selection and molecular evolution in PTC, a bitter-taste receptor gene. *American Journal of Human Genetics,* 74(4): 637-646.

UTM Biology Faculty Profile:

Dr. Joel Levine studies the genetic basis of social dynamics in the fruit fly, *Drosophila melanogaster*, including the influence of circadian clocks, recognition, communication and other interactive phenotypes.

Recent Publications:

Schneider, J., Dickinson, M.H., and Levine, J.D. 2012. Social structures depend on innate determinants and chemosensory processing in *Drosophila. Proceeding of the National Academy of Science,* (in press).

Schneider, J., Atallah, J., and Levine, J.D. 2012. One, two, and many—A perspective on what groups of Drosophila *melanogaster* can tell us about social dynamics. *Advances in Genetics,* (in press).

Krupp, J.J. and Levine, J.D. 2010. Biological Rhythms: The Taste-Time Continuum. *Current Biology,* 20(4): R147-R149.

Billeter, J., Atallah, J., Krupp, J.J., Millar, J.G. and Levine, J.D. 2009. Specialized cells tag sexual and species identity in *Drosophila melanogaster. Nature,* 461(7266): 987-U250.

Krupp, J.J., Kent, C., Billeter, J., Azanchi, R., So, A.K.-., Schonfeld, J.A., Smith, B.P., Lucas, C. and Levine, J.D., 2008. Social experience modifies pheromone expression and mating behavior in male *Drosophila melanogaster. Current Biology,* 18(18): 1373-1383.

For more information on Dr. Levine's lab, research and publications, visit his website at:
http://www.utm.utoronto.ca/biology/people/levine-joel

Bacteria and Antibiotic Resistance

The lab 6 assignment involves the completion of a group worksheet (found via the 'Labs' link on the course Blackboard site.

During the first week of the Bacteria and Antibiotic Resistance Lab, you will be setting up your bacterial plates. You will be reviewing your results and completing your worksheet(s) in lab the following week.

Overview

In this laboratory exercise you **work in groups of 4** to determine the ability of antiseptics, antibiotics, disinfectants, and household food items on inhibiting the growth of E. coli by utilizing the zone of inhibition test.

Preparation

1. Read through the entire lab and associated worksheet(s).
2. Read Appendix 6 regarding using sterile technique when handling and plating bacteria.
3. Review textbook chapter 24.
4. Lab coats are recommended for this lab.

Laboratory Objectives

After completing this laboratory exercise, you should be able to:
1. Explain the difference between antiseptics, disinfectants, and antibiotics.
2. Define and understand the following key terms: resistance, sensitivity, antimicrobial, bactericidal, bacteriostatic, zone of inhibition, pathogen, sterilization.
3. Discuss the relative effectiveness of antiseptics, disinfectants, antibiotics, and household food items to control bacterial growth based on the size of the zone of inhibition.

4. Perform sterile lab techniques.

5. Answer the questions below:

Which antimicrobial is the most effective at controlling *E. coli* growth?
Which was the least effective?

Background Information

Bacteria are ubiquitous; they are found almost everywhere. Some bacteria are beneficial and are used in making various products including cheeses, yogurt and some alcohols (including biofuels like ethanol). The human digestive system is home to numerous beneficial bacteria that help us digest our food and even make some vitamins. Some bacteria can be harmful, or pathogenic, and cause disease. Bacterial diseases include tuberculosis, pneumonia, and tetanus in humans, as well as leaf spots or fire blight in plants.

Bacteria have a very short generation time (approximately 20 minutes under ideal conditions) and reproduce asexually via binary fission. Binary fission is the process by which a cell divides to produce two genetically identical cells. Even though bacteria reproduce asexually, there are mechanisms that may introduce genetic variability between individuals. Bacteria can generate new alleles through mutations that occur approximately once every 250,000 cell divisions. Such mutations may result in an allele associated with resistance to a specific antibiotic. Bacteria can also move small amounts of DNA from one individual to another through horizontal gene transfer. This is not a form of reproduction but simply the movement of DNA between individual cells in a bacterial community. This transfer of DNA can occur between members of the same species or between different bacterial species.

Remember that when there is variation among individuals in a trait that influences their ability to survive and reproduce, natural selection favours individuals with more adaptive (i.e., more beneficial) versions of the trait. If this adaptive characteristic is genetically based, natural selection can result in evolution (i.e., a change in the frequency of a heritable trait as it passes from one generation to the next). In many microbial populations, individual bacterial cells differ in their resistance to particular antibiotics. This resistance is often a function of proteins that have been coded for by bacterial DNA. Therefore, variation in resistance to antibiotics is heritable and can evolve in response to natural selection.

In addition, evolution in response to natural selection is a response of a population to an interaction between individuals and their environment. If the particular antibiotic is not present in the environment, resistance to it does not increase bacterial survival and reproduction, and so the frequency of resistant individuals does not increase in the population. The evolution of bacteria resistant to antibiotics depends on genetic variation between individual bacteria that influences their level of resistance.

Bacterial Sensitivity to Antimicrobials (Plating)

Description:

Some common physical methods of controlling bacterial growth include sterilization, freezing, desiccation, and irradiation. However, in this laboratory activity, you will examine the ability of a number of chemical treatments to control growth of the bacteria *Escherichia coli* (*E. coli*). Chemical methods for controlling bacterial growth involve the use of antimicrobial agents such as antiseptics, disinfectants, antibiotics and even some common foods and spices (see Table 6.1). These treatments can either result in killing the bacteria (bactericidal) or inhibiting the growth of the bacteria (bacteriostatic).

Antibiotics are substances that are produced by or derived from microorganisms that destroy or interfere with the development of another organism. Common examples of antibiotics are penicillin and streptomycin, produced by a fungus (*Penicillium*) and a bacterium (*Streptomyces*) respectively. During the past 70 years, the widespread use of antibiotics to fight bacterial pathogens has saved millions of lives. However, the ability of antibiotics to kill populations of bacterial pathogens is declining due to the evolution of bacterial resistance.

Antiseptics (e.g., antibacterial soaps and rubbing alcohol) inhibit the growth of the infectious agents, like bacteria, and are harmless enough that they can be applied to the skin but should not be ingested.

Disinfectants (e.g., ammonia and bleach) eliminate or destroy pathogenic microorganisms, with the exception of bacterial spores. Disinfectants should not be applied to skin and should never be ingested.

Table 6.1
Antimicrobials that will be used in this laboratory exercise.

Antibiotics	Antiseptics	Disinfectants	Household food items
Neomycin	Hydrogen peroxide	Ammonia	Vinegar
Penicillin	Listerine®	Lysol®	Lemon juice
Streptomycin	Antibacterial soap	10% bleach	Oregano Oil
Ampicillin	Rubbing Alcohol	Dish Soap	Hot sauce

Some common **foods and spices** contain bioactive compounds, including phenolics, flavonoids, sterols, and essential oils that have been demonstrated to have antimicrobial properties.

Materials:

1. 4 Nutrient Agar (NA) plates—one for each treatment
2. *E. coli* (strain #10) liquid bacterial culture
3. Sterile swabs for inoculating each plate with bacteria.
4. Sterile control discs—handle carefully! These need to remain as sterile as possible so cannot be dropped.
5. Additional materials: Antimicrobial substances, a pen, parafilm, forceps, 95% alcohol, alcohol burner.

Procedure:

1. Wash your hands with soap and water.
2. Wipe down your bench area with 70% EtOH and paper towels.
3. Each group member chooses 1 set of variables (antibiotics, antiseptic, disinfectants, or household food items) to test (see Table 6.1).
4. Using the sharpie marker, label each of your plates accordingly. Make sure to label the plate and NOT the lid! (see Figure 6.1).
   a. Label the side of each agar plate with **lab section**, **TA name**, **lab room #** and the **name of your group** (Figure 6.1A).
   b. On the bottom of each plate, write a 'C' at the center of the plate. This indicates where you will place your sterile control disc. Write the first letter of each of the chosen compounds for that particular treatment evenly spaced around the 'C'. Your treatment labels/discs should be roughly equidistant from each other, the control disc and the edge of the test plate (Figure 6.1B).

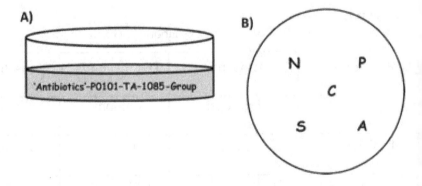

Figure 6.1
Using the antibiotic plate as an example of how to label each your experimental plates. (A) How to label the side of the <u>antibiotic</u> plate with your lab section, TA name, lab room number and unique group name. (B) How to label the bottom of the antibiotic plate with the first letter of each chosen antibiotic (neomycin [N], penicillin [P], streptomycin [S], ampicillin [A]). C stands for where you will place the sterile disc in the centre of the plate to serve as the control.

5. Each person in your group will prepare a bacterial lawn on <u>one</u> plate (See Figure 6.2). *Using the following steps, ensure that bacteria have been evenly applied to the entire surface of the test plate as bare patches will confound your results. If you leave bare patches, you will not be able to tell if your antimicrobial treatment has actually been effective or if you are not seeing any growth because there were never any bacteria in the area to begin with due to your sloppy plating technique.*

   a. Insert a sterile swab into the bacterial culture and allow it to become saturated with liquid.

   b. Allow the swab to stop dripping before you remove the swab from the culture tube.

   c. Lift the lid of your plate to about 45° and gently <u>swab the entire surface</u> of the agar, right to the edge of the dish. Be sure to apply the bacteria evenly over the entire surface of the agar (Figure 6.2A).

   d. Rotate the plate 90 degrees and swab again, again ensuring that the bacteria are applied evenly to the entire surface (Figure 6.2B).

   e. Cover the plate with the lid and set aside carefully.

   f. Dispose of the swab in the biohazard waste container.

6. Set up each of your test plates with the chosen antibiotics, disinfectants, antiseptics, or household food items using the following steps:

   a. Light your burner and keep it well away from your 95% alcohol.

   b. Dip a pair of forceps into 95% alcohol. *The purpose of the alcohol is to sterilize the forceps.*

   c. Flame the forceps briefly using the burner. *The purpose of the flame is to burn off the 95% alcohol. It is very important not to heat the forceps.*

   d. Use the sterilized forceps to pick up a control disc and place it in position 'C' on your plate. **Do not move the disc around once it has been placed on the plate.** *When you examine your test plates next week, you should observe bacterial growth around the control disc. If a zone of inhibition (i.e., area of no bacterial growth) is observed around your control disc, the effectiveness of the other microbial treatments will be in question; you would not know if lack of bacterial growth around the treatment discs was due to the known antimicrobial used or by some unknown property/contamination of the paper discs themselves.*

   e. Repeat steps a-d for each of your test discs making sure that you allow the excess liquid to drain before placing the discs onto your test plate.

Figure 6.2
An example of how to prepare a bacterial lawn for each experimental plate.
(A) Using the soaked bacterial swab, swab the entire surface of the agar plate, ensuring that you reach the edges of the dish. (B) Rotate the plate 90° and swab the entire surface of the agar again.

7. Seal each plate with a strip of parafilm.

8. Put your plates in the designated tray **with the lid up**. This is to ensure that the discs do not come loose, but normally bacterial plates would be kept with the lid down to prevent condensation from dripping onto the cultures.

9. Plates will be stored at 37°C for 24 hours to allow the bacteria to grow. The plates will then be stored at 4°C to impede further bacterial growth until next lab, when you will view your plates measure the zone of inhibition for each treatment (see Activity 6.2).

10. Wash bench area with 70% EtOH.

11. Wash your hands with soap and water.

ACTIVITY 6.2
Bacterial Sensitivity to Antimicrobials (Results Analysis)

Description:

You will evaluate the effectiveness of each of the antimicrobial treatments by utilizing the zone of inhibition test. If the chosen agents have antimicrobial activity, then a zone of inhibition will be apparent around the antimicrobial-soaked disc (Figure 6.3). The zone of inhibition (ZOI) is where there is minimal or no bacterial growth and the size of the ZOI relates to the potency or effectiveness of the antimicrobial. If the bacteria are resistant to the antimicrobial agent, then growth of the bacteria will occur right to the edge of the disc. In some cases, you may observe a few small, discrete colonies within a large ZOI; these colonies could represent the descendants of single resistant bacterium that was present in the initial bacterial culture or the descendants of an individual that obtained a mutant resistance allele at some point during the experiment.

Figure 6.3
Example showing a zone of inhibition (ZOI—white area). The zone of inhibition is calculated by measuring the diameter of the ZOI, as indicated by the double-headed arrow. Filled black circle represents the disc soaked with antimicrobial agent and the grey area indicates area of bacterial growth.

Procedure:

1. Wash your hands with soap and water.
2. Wipe down your bench area with 70% EtOH and paper towels.
3. Retrieve your experimental plates from your TA. **NOTE: *It should not be necessary to remove the lids from the plates to view bacterial growth and measure the ZOI for each treatment.***
4. Examine the plates and complete the Lab 6 worksheet.
5. Discard your bacterial plates in the appropriate biohazard containers.
6. Wash bench area with 70% EtOH.
7. Wash your hands with soap and water.

Check Your Understanding:

1. What are some characteristics of bacteria that enable them to quickly develop antibiotic resistance?
2. Why is it important to clean your working area and hands before beginning the experiment?
3. Why is it important that your bacterial lawn cover the whole plate?
4. Why do the bacterial plates need to be incubated initially at higher temperature for a short period of time and then in a cool environment?
5. What physical method of controlling bacterial growth did you use? Why did you need to use it?
6. Do you expect to see bacterial growth around the control disc when you examine your plates? What would a ZOI around the control disc tell you about the validity of your experimental results?
7. Would you expect to see largest ZOI around the most effective antimicrobial or the least effective antimicrobial compound?
8. How would you interpret the presence of small colonies with a ZOI?

Apply What You Know:

Think about the symbiotic relationship you have with the intestinal flora (microorganisms—mostly bacteria) that lives within your digestive system. These bacteria have multiple functions, including helping with digestion and absorption of some nutrients, repressing the growth of pathogenic microbes, aiding with immunity, and helping synthesize vitamins. The environment within your digestive tract is constantly changing. How can your bacteria keep up with this constantly changing environment? Would taking an antibiotic affect all of the bacterial species in your digestive tract?

Why Is This Important?

Bacterial resistance to treatment by antibiotics is a serious public health issue and can only be effectively addressed if medical professionals, farmers, and the general public become more aware of the principles of evolution in response to natural selection. Additionally, understanding recommendations on the appropriate use of antibiotics involves learning about the unique and subtle methods by which microbes transfer bits of genetic information.

Additional Investigations and Applications:

- Metagenomics is an emerging field of research where genomic material is collected directly from an environmental sample and is analyzed, such as a water sample from the ocean. This emerging field would allow the analysis of DNA from populations that are not easily cultivated in a laboratory and would broaden our understanding of the genetics of organisms like certain microbes. Understanding the genetics of a greater number of species of microbes may enable the development of better antimicrobials.

- To increase genetic diversity in bacterial populations, bacteria exchange genetic material through horizontal gene transfer. There are three mechanisms that bacteria utilize in horizontal gene transfer: conjugation, transduction, and transformation. Briefly, Conjugation involves the transfer of genetic material from one bacterium to another through direct cell-to-cell contact. On the other hand, transduction is the injection of DNA into a bacterium by a virus, whereas transformation is the uptake, incorporation, and expression of short fragments of DNA. Bacteria that are able to undergo transformation are termed competent. In a laboratory setting, bacterial cells can be treated chemically so that foreign DNA or plasmids can be incorporated into the cells. These competent bacterial cells can be used for various molecular applications such as cloning.

- Bacteria living in extremely harsh environments are challenging what we know about what might make up hospitable living conditions, here on Earth and on other planets. A couple of years ago, bacteria living in Mono Lake in California were discovered. These bacteria, known as GFAJ-1, are poison-eating; they thrive on arsenic. These bacteria actually utilize arsenic, normally deadly to the living, in photosynthesis instead of water. Not only are these bacteria substituting arsenic for water, but they are also substituting the arsenic for phosphorus! So this raises the question: If a living thing on Earth can do something so unheard of, what else can life do? How does this discovery change how we explore for life on other planets?

Additional Resource:

- You also might look at the comparison of antibacterial and regular soap from HowStuffWorks:
http://health.howstuffworks.com/question692.htm

UTM Biology Faculty Profile

Dr. George Espie is a Professor in the Department of Biology at UTM and is a faculty member in the Department of Cell and Systems Biology at the University of Toronto. Dr. Espie's research focus is microbial physiology and biochemistry with interest in photosynthesis. In his research, Dr. Espie investigates the carbon dioxide-concentrating mechanism of cyanobacteria.

Recent Publications:

- Peña, K.L, Castel, S.E., de Araujo, C., Espie, G.S. 2010. Structural basis of the oxidative activation of the carboxysomal γ-carbonic anhydrase, CcmM. PNAS, 107: 2455-2460.
- Cisek, R., Spencer, L., Prent, N., Zigmantas, D., Espie, G.S., Barzda, V. 2010. Optical microscopy in photosynthesis. Photosynthesis Research, 102: 111-141.
- Cot, S.S-W., So, A.K-C., Espie, G. 2008. A multiprotein bicarbonate dehydration complex essential to carboxysome function in cyanobacteria. Journal of Bacteriology, 190: 936-945.

For more information on Dr. Espie's lab, research and publications, visit his website at:

http://utm.utoronto.ca/BIOLOGY/PEOPLE/ESPIE-GEORGE

BIO152 Laboratory 7
Sexual Selection

The lab 7 assignment involves the completion of an individual assignment (assignment details and templates are found via the 'Labs' link on the course Blackboard site). Your assignment is due at the beginning of your regular lab section next week.

** Please be very quiet when entering the laboratory so that the crickets are not disturbed. The lights in the lab will be off and only red lights will be on so that stress on the crickets is kept to a minimum.

Overview

In this laboratory exercise you will work in pairs to conduct experiments to test hypotheses about courtship behaviours in crickets.

Preparation

1. Read through the entire lab and associated assignment instructions.
2. Review textbook chapter 25.

Laboratory Objectives

After completing this laboratory exercise, you should be able to:

1. Define intrasexual and intersexual competition
2. Explain why/how intersexual and intrasexual competition affects morphology and behaviour. Why is there asymmetric morphology between the sexes?
3. Evaluate the direct and indirect benefits for females when choosing a mate through female choice.
4. Determine the answer to the following experimental questions:

What characteristics or behaviours make a male cricket better able to compete in a fight?

What characteristics or behaviours exhibited by the male cricket did a female seem to prefer?

Background Information

In 1859 Charles Darwin first introduced the concept of **sexual selection** in his book 'On the Origin of Species' and further fleshed out his theory in 'The Descent of Man, and Selection in Relation to Sex'. Darwin based this theory on the observation that many male animals developed exaggerated features, such as beautiful male peacock feathers, expansive male deer antlers, or the large mane of a male lion. The primary function of these exaggerated features is to increase the reproductive success of the males that adorn them by acting as weapons during same-sex combat to gain access to potential mates or by acting as indicators of sexual vigor and quality during courtship behaviours.

Unlike natural selection, which stems from the struggle to survive, sexual selection stems from the struggle to reproduce, and acts on an organism's ability to obtain and successfully copulate with a mate. There are two ways that sexual selection can work: male competition or female choice (but keep in mind, there are examples of sex role reversals in nature). There are many facets to male competition, or **intrasexual selection**. Not only does intrasexual selection involve males competing for access to females, but also for copulation time and even sperm competition. On the other hand female choice, or **intersexual selection**, occurs when a female chooses a mate, as well as facets of copulation such as how long mating will occur and which sperm to utilize when fertilizing eggs.

Since opportunities for breeding are complicated by short and seasonal breeding periods, number of offspring that can be born at one time, and even food availability, females can be very picky when choosing a mate. But these are not the only factors that affect a female's choice of mate. Females invest a lot of energy into gamete production, gestation, as well as care of offspring, while males tend to invest a lot less in the production of gametes and tend not to care for offspring. Thus, females use ornamentation, or exaggerated features, to help with their decision for choosing a mate. Females often view a male with elaborate ornamentation as more fit.

ACTIVITY 7.1

Intrasexual and Intersexual Selection in Crickets

Description:

For this activity, you will work in pairs to observe the sexually dimorphic morphology and behaviour of male and female crickets. After your initial observations you will determine if larger males are dominant to smaller males in an intrasexual selection scenario and which males are preferred by females in an intersexual selection scenario.

Crickets are sexually dimorphic, as evidenced by the differences in morphology of some external structures. For instance, the easiest way to identify female crickets is by the long ovipositor that is used to lay eggs. Another difference between the two sexes is exhibited on the wings. Male crickets use their wings to produce sounds during stridulation, while female crickets do not produce sounds. Male cricket wings are elaborate, with modifications for sound production including a robust vein covered with a comb of 'teeth' along the bottom margin of each wing. Male crickets are capable of producing different songs, including a calling song to attract females, a courting song, as well as an aggressive song that is produced in the presence of other male crickets.

Male crickets are territorial insects with respect to space as well as resources and will use aggressive behaviours if they feel threatened or if they want to exert dominance over other male crickets. Some of these aggressive behaviours include:

- Standing in a straight upright position
- Pushing an opponent with the hind legs
- Push-ups' or body shaking
- Aggressive stridulation that is loud and sounds scratchy
- Mandible flaring or opening of the mouth
- Physical fighting or grappling
- Attenation or strikes of the antennae across the body of an opponent

Materials:

1. Male and female crickets
2. Observation chamber
3. Other materials: pen/pencil, raw data & observation sheets, timer

Procedure:

Part 1: Examining male and female morphology [~10 minutes].

1. Each pair of students should choose 2 male crickets and 1 female cricket
2. Observe the female cricket and note her sexually dimorphic features. In particular, make sure that you can see the ovipositor (your TA will help you if you are having difficulty) and make sure that you can tell the difference between your male and female crickets.
3. Observe each pair of male crickets carefully and note the morphology of each. Your intrasexual selection (male-male competition) experiment will be based on size and determine whether the larger cricket is dominant to the smaller cricket. Make sure that you can tell your male crickets apart.

Part 2: Examining intrasexual selection (male-male competition) and recording observations. [~30 minutes]

1. Carefully place one male cricket on either side of the opaque divider of the observation arena. Make sure that you keep track of which is the "small" male and which is the "large" male.

2. Wait 5 minutes for the crickets to adjust to the new environment.

3. Lift the opaque divider to release the two male crickets into the observation arena to observe each cricket's activity level and aggressive behaviours **for a period of 15 minutes**.

4. After 15 minutes of observation, slide the opaque divider back into the arena to separate the male crickets being careful not to damage them.

5. While waiting for the males to recover, you can finish recording your observations regarding the activity level and behaviours for each cricket in the space provided in Table 7.1.

   Observations may include, but are not limited to:
   - how long it took for the two male crickets to interact
   - which cricket initiated the fight (if there was one)
   - what parts of the body did each cricket use
   - which aggressive behaviours were exhibited
   - how long the fight lasted, what each cricket did after the fight
   - which cricket was dominant
   - whether one of the crickets was more submissive and tried to avoid fighting with the other male
   - compare the activity level of each male—do they stay in one spot or move around?
   - Indicate if a fight occurred

6. Record which male (small or large) was dominant in the class data table on the chalkboard. Remember to copy all of the information in the class data table on the chalkboard into Table 7.3 BEFORE you leave the lab today. You will need this data to complete your assignment.

Part 3: Examining intersexual selection (female choice) and recording observations. [~30 minutes]

1. Place one male cricket on either side of the opaque divider of the observation arena.

2. Allow the female to be visible to each of the male crickets during this time. Wait 5 minutes for the crickets to adjust to the new environment.

3. Lift the opaque divider between the two males and place the female cricket into the observation arena.

4. For **15 minutes**, observe each male cricket's activity level and aggressive behaviours. Also assess the behaviours of the female cricket and record your observations in Table 7.2. *Note that if a copulation attempt is successful, the female will mount the male.*

   Observations can include, but are not limited to:
   - how long it took for the two male crickets to interact
   - which cricket initiated the fight (if there was one),
   - what parts of the body did each cricket use
   - which aggressive behaviours were exhibited
   - how long the fight lasted, what each cricket did after the fight,
   - which cricket was dominant
   - whether one of the crickets was more submissive and tried to avoid fighting with the other male

- compare the activity level of each male – do they stay in one spot or move around?
- indicate if a fight occurred
- comment on the female cricket's behaviour and activity level.

5. Record which male (small or large) was chosen by the female in the class data table on the chalkboard. Remember to copy all of the information in the class data table on the chalkboard into Table 7.4 BEFORE you leave the lab today. You will need this data to complete your assignment.

6. Remove your crickets from the arena and return them to their appropriate holding containers (as indicated by your TA).

Observation tables for your experiments:

Table 7.1
Observations for the intrasexual (male-male) competition experiment.

Cricket 1 ("small")	Cricket 2 ("large")
- wings flapping when the large cricket approach the small one for fighting.	- more active - freely moving around the arena
Which cricket was more aggressive/dominant?	

Table 7.2
Observations for the intersexual (female choice) experiment.

Female Cricket	Male Cricket 1 ("small")	Male Cricket 2 ("large")
Hops on to of small the male	- Keeps flapping to get the female. - trying hard to get her	—
Which male did the female chose?		

Summary tables for class results (*Record the class data BEFORE you leave the lab today*):

Table 7.3
Intrasexual selection (male-male) results.

Trial	Student Names	Most aggressive/dominant Male (small or large)
1		
2		
3		
4		
5		
6		
7		
8		
9		
10		
11		
12		

Table 7.4
Intersexual selection (female choice) results.

Trial	Student Names	Which male did the female chose? (small, large, or neither) (yes or no).	Was the chosen male the more aggressive/dominant male?
1			
2			
3			
4			
5			
6			
7			
8			
9			
10			
11			
12			

Check Your Understanding:

1. What is the difference between sexual selection and natural selection? What is the relationship between them?

2. What is the difference between intersexual selection and intrasexual selection?

3. How does male-male competition lead to the evolution of large body size or 'weapon-like' features in some males?

4. Why are males usually the sex with ornamentation used in courtship?

5. Why are females usually the choosier sex? Discuss gamete production, parental investment, and potential number of offspring.

6. Sexual selection can sometimes produce features that are not conducive to the individual's survival. Why might this occur? Can you think of an example of this?

7. Why do you need to observe the activity and behaviours of the crickets before you begin your experiments?

8. Why did you need to acclimatize the crickets to the observation arena before starting the experiment?

9. Why did you leave the female visible to the male crickets during the acclimation time to the observation arena?

Apply What You Know:

A parasitoid is an insect whose larval stage parasitizes and eventually kills another insect host. Some parasitoids target crickets. How might these parasitoids find their cricket hosts? Do you think one sex would be at a greater risk of parasitism due to sexual selection? Why or why not?

Why Is This Important?

The theory of sexual selection and how sexual selection operates is important to understand due to the influence that it has on evolution. Consider a man who did not mate during his lifetime. Any beneficial genes he possessed will now be lost since he did not have any offspring to pass those genes on to. Now consider a man that produces two offspring. He is able to pass on his genes to his children, who subsequently pass them on to their offspring and so on. Thus, the man's fitness is higher than the first man who did not mate, in which his fitness is zero. Thus, sexual selection can highly affect the evolution of species.

Additional Investigations and Applications:

• Mutual mate choice—how does sexual selection work in both sexes?

• The evolution of multiple sexually selected traits and preferences—how does a female choose the traits to assess and how does she assess these multiple traits to select a mate?

• Why are there more exaggerated differences between the sexes of some species than others?

• Many animals use pheromones, or airborne chemicals, to communicate during mating. How might these pheromones influence the choice of a mate?

• What is the genetic basis of sexual selection?

References:

Adamo S.A., Hoy R.R. 1995. Agonistic behaviour in male and female field crickets, *Gryllus bimaculatus*, and how behavioural context influences its expression. Animal Behaviour, 49:1491-1501.

Burk T. 1983. Male aggression and female choice in a field cricket (*Teleogryllus oceanicus*): the importance of courtship song. In: Gwynne DT, Morris GK, editors. Orthopteran mating systems: sexual competition in a diverse group of insects. Boulder, Colorado: Westview Press. p. 97-119.

Hofmann, H.A., Schildberger, K. 2001. Assessment of strength and willingness to fight during aggressive encounters in crickets. Animal Behaviour, 62:337-348

UTM Biology Faculty Profile

Dr. Gwynne is a Professor in the Department of Biology at UTM and is a faculty member in the Department of Ecology and Evolutionary Biology at the University of Toronto. Dr. Gwynne uses insects and spiders to understand sexual selection. This includes measurements in the wild of sexual and natural selection on female ornamentation to address the question of why sex-specific ornaments are rare in females.

Recent Publications:

- Gwynne, D.T., Kelly, C.D. 2011. Weta Sex: Fast and Furious. Forest and Bird Magazine (New Zealand), May: pp 20-23.
- Robson, L.J., Gwynne, D.T. 2010. Measuring sexual selection on females in sex-role-reversed Mormon crickets (*Anabrus simplex*, Orthoptera: Tettigoniidae). Journal of Evolutionary Biology, 23(7): 1528-1537.
- Ursprung, C., den Hollander, M., Gwynne, D.T. 2009. Female seed beetles, *Callosobruchus maculates*, remate for male-supplied water rather than ejaculate nutrition. Behavioural Ecology and Sociobiology, 63(6): 781-788.
- Gwynne, D.T. 2008. Sexual conflict over nuptial gifts in insects. Annual Review of Entomology, 53: 83-101.

For more information on Dr. Gwynne's lab, research and publications, visit his website at: http://labs.eeb.utoronto.ca/gwynne/

BIO152 Case Study
Presentations

Procedure:

1. Your TA will assign case studies to each lab group for 4 students.

2. Read through the case study and outline the approach you will take to exploring the case.

3. Prepare an oral PowerPoint presentation based on your assigned case. Your presentation should be 7 minutes in length. All PowerPoint slides must be properly referenced, as appropriate (**see Appendix 2**). All images must contain an appropriate citation. Also refer to your book *A Short Guide to Writing About Biology* for referencing instructions.

4. During the case study presentations, you will evaluate your peers using the **Peer Evaluation Form** found on Blackboard.

5. At the end of the case study presentations, please evaluate the contribution of your group members using the **Group Evaluation Form** found on Blackboard.

(1) What is a case?

A case is a type of scenario that is useful for learning. In general, cases are created in many formats including videos, computer-based programs, and written forms. Text-based cases, such as the ones in this book, are common and they can be one paragraph or many pages long. In this book, the cases are about a page long.

Following is an example of a short biology case similar to ones you will find in this book.

Case: *Derrick's Malaise*

About a month after returning home from a season of fieldwork in Guatemala, Derrick began to feel sick again. His roommate took him to the clinic. They were both worried that he was having a recurrence of the malaria he had contracted on the trip.

"How could I have these symptoms again?" Derrick asked the resident, Dr. Welty. "I finished the prescription they gave me in Guatemala and I have been feeling fine."

"I'm not sure why you have this again," Dr. Welty replied. "We'll need a blood sample so we can analyze the organism to see what

---

strain it is. In the meantime, let's try a different drug. I'm going to switch you to chloroquine." He continued, "You know, malaria is one of the most common infectious diseases in the world. I've got some contacts at the CDC who may be interested in your relapse. May I share your records with them?"

"I wonder if I can get malaria from Derrick," wondered Derrick's roommate, who was flipping through magazines in the waiting room.

Case Authors: Ethel Stanley and Margaret Waterman, 2001. Investigative Cases and Case Based Learning in Biology, version 1.0, in Jungck and Vaughan (Eds.), BioQUEST Library VI. San Diego: Academic Press.

(2) How do I begin?

Begin by finding out what the case is about. Read through the case to get a sense of the story and issues. If you are working in a group, try having one person read the case aloud while the others read along silently. This may sound unusual, but it helps everyone in the group focus on the case.

(3) What is the Case Analysis all about?

Once your group has read the case, go to the Case Analysis sheet found just after each case. Case Analysis helps you to identify the main ideas in the case, as well as what you already know about the situation, and what your questions are about the case. If you analyze the case in a group, you will share your ideas, hear what others are thinking, and have a good sense of what the group needs to learn about this case. Case Analysis involves four steps.

Step A. Recognize potential issues and major topics in the case.

Go back and read the case again, this time highlighting or underlining words or phrases that seem to be important to understanding the situation. Look for issues that you might explore further. Jot down your ideas and questions about these words and phrases. If you are working in a group, this approach might be done as a group discussion, with one person keeping a list of issues as they are also raised. At this point, you are also answering the question, "What is this case about?"

The following is an example of the kinds of issues raised in the case *Derrick's Malaise.*

What does the case seem to be about? Malaria, how it is caused, why it might reoccur, how it is treated, and how it is transmitted.

What are some potential issues? How malarial drugs work, Derrick's relapse, worldwide rates of malarial infections, the role of the CDC.

Step B. What specific questions do you have about these topics?
In this step of Case Analysis, you will share what you already know, or what you think you know, and you will raise your questions. The "Know/Need to Know" chart, found in each Case Analysis, is a way to organize your thoughts. An example is included on the next page.

Use Case Analysis as a brainstorming session. You can refer back to the underlined words and phrases in the case as a way to help organize this discussion. This step can be accomplished alone; however, experience shows it is better done in a group.

Using the *Derrick's Malaise* case as an example, here are some questions raised by learners who have worked with this case:

What Do I Know?	What Do I Need to Know?
• Malaria is transmitted by mosquitoes.	• Why was Derrick in Guatemala?
• It is found in locations that are warm and damp.	• How common is malaria—worldwide, Guatemala, United States?
• It isn't common today in the United States.	• What role does the CDC have?
• It can be treated with drugs.	• What kind of organism causes malaria?
• You can get better.	• Should Derrick's roommate be concerned?
• It can recur (from the case).	• What is chloroquine? Is it a common drug? How does it work? Is it safe?
• It is caused by a microorganism.	• What other drugs are used?
• The CDC is the Centers for Disease Control and Prevention.	• How do you prevent malaria?
• Many people die of malaria each year.	• Do all types of mosquitoes transmit malaria?
	• What strains of the malarial organism are there?
	• Is it okay for the doctor to switch drugs without knowing more?

Step C. Assign priority to the questions.
Review the questions listed on the "What Do I Need to Know?" side of the chart. It is very likely that your brainstorming session raised many different kinds of questions on many topics related to the case (but not necessarily to biology). Go over your list and put a check by the three questions that seem most important to understanding this case. One way to do this is to think about which questions fit with the topics on your course syllabus or in the textbook chapters being studied. Check off those questions as well as others that interest you the most.

> If *Derrick's Malaise* was introduced while you were reading a chapter on microorganisms, questions about the organism causing malaria would be fairly important to investigate. Other questions that you find interesting but that are not linked to a syllabus topic may also be chosen for study, such as "How does chloroquine work?"

You will find that some of your questions may be addressed in the investigations that accompany the case. You might also have questions that this Case Book does not address. Your instructor might suggest that you expand on these questions by developing a paper, presentation, experiment, ethics statement, or other product.

"One of the greatest challenges in biology is to frame appropriate and productive questions that can be pursued by the technology at hand. You have probably had a great deal of experience in solving pre-posed problems, such as those found at the end of textbook chapters. However, if you were asked to go into a lab or out in a field and pose a research question, you will find that this is often difficult to do without some practice . . ."

(The BioQUEST Library IV: *A Note to the Student*, University of Maryland Press, 1996)

Step D. What kinds of references or resources would help you answer or explore these questions?

No matter what questions you investigate, it is likely you will seek and use resources to help you develop persuasive answers. It is important to develop the habit of thinking broadly about where you might go to find answers to your questions. Resources may include your textbooks, other library materials, computer simulations, results of lab or field research, articles, data sets, maps, e-mails, pamphlets from organizations, interviews with experts, or museum exhibits. Be creative, but remember your data are only as good as your sources.

For *Derrick's Malaise,* you might choose to examine:

- Maps of malaria prevalence

- A reference book such as *Physicians' Desk Reference* to find out how chloroquine works

- A Web page from the CDC with international travel precautions

- Your textbook index for relevant terms

- A simulation in which the prevalence of different species of competing mosquitoes is examined under different conditions

- An interview with a person who has had malaria

You will find links to a variety of online resources referenced in the cases on the Campbell website (http://www.masteringbiology.com) under the tab marked "Case Book." In addition to the resources organized by case, you will find additional open-ended investigations where you can pose your own questions.

(4) What do I do after the Case Analysis?

Each case is accompanied by several investigations. Your instructor might assign just one or two of the available investigations, depending on what fits best in your course. You can also use this book independently. You might complete the Case Analysis and selected investigations as a way to check your own knowledge.

(5) What if my instructor wants me to develop my own investigations?

Your group is likely to raise different questions in the case analysis from the ones investigated in this book. Sometimes an instructor might ask you to follow up your own question in a lab or to design an investigation of your choice. Following is some advice on ways to turn your case-related questions into scientific investigations.

A. Getting started: How do I develop my question?

As you develop the problem and questions you want to use to investigate and learn more about the topics, it will be important for you to consult with others, such as members of your group or other classmates. Discussing your ideas and plans is an important step in refining problems and can lead you to different perspectives and possible good research problems. Continue this practice of sharing with others as you gather evidence for your problem and as you prepare to present your conclusions. This kind of communication is the standard among scientists.

B. What am I expected to do with my question(s)?

Once you have a problem you want to investigate, you and your instructor might consider any of the following:

- Design and conduct new investigations utilizing laboratory or field methods.

- Use computer software modules, spreadsheets, simulations, data sets, interactive maps, remote sensing, or graphics to investigate the question.

- Seek new sources of data (further references, interviews, data sets).

- Develop an investigation that builds from a standard lab exercise, perhaps by changing the independent variable or establishing new controls.

Following are three possible investigations for *Derrick's Malaise.*

1. Work with a simulation to investigate hypotheses about control of mosquitoes that carry malaria-causing organisms. Nonvector mosquitoes can be introduced to compete with the vectors.
2. Use genomics tools and the PlasmoDB (a database of gene sequences from many species of *Plasmodium*) to examine genes in resistant and nonresistant strains of *Plasmodium falciparum.*
3. Develop an experiment to test the effectiveness of controlling mosquito populations with fish that feed on larvae.

C. When am I finished?

". . . You must confront the issue of closure in research. How do you know when you have a 'right' answer? When is research done? Scientists do not arrive at a final answer; usually research is abandoned for a variety of reasons, including time, resources, and most importantly, when the scientific research team is 'satisfied' with their conclusions, that is, when the solution is 'useful' for some purpose."
(The BioQUEST Library IV: *A Note to the Student,* University of Maryland Press, 1996)

When you are ready to present your conclusions, remember that you need to persuade others of the value of your methodologies and data. Consider your audience carefully as you develop products to support your conclusions, such as

- Scientific posters
- Advertisements urging political action
- Videos defining the issues for the public
- Pamphlets/brochures with recommendations for a specific user group
- Consulting reports (if you are role-playing)
- Art work, such as cartoons, revealing issues from the case
- Designs for a new technological approach to the problem
- Scientific reports to local or regional groups
- A new case study to emphasize your findings

> "Research is not complete, no matter how many experiments have been conducted, no matter how many puzzles have been solved, until peers outside of a research team are persuaded of the utility of the answers. Persuasion is a social process and an essential one for you to experience in order to understand the nature of scientific theories and paradigm shifts. Communication in the science community is an active process full of controversy and debate. The productive side of science involves open criticism of the methods and conclusions made by a research group. This controversy and debate is important to the creation and acceptance of new scientific knowledge."
>
> (The BioQUEST Library IV: *A Note to the Student,* University of Maryland, 1996)

D. How will our group work be assessed and evaluated?

Like many students, you probably have concerns about the assessment and evaluation methods used in group work, especially in scientific inquiry.

Peer review is a key feature of how scientists judge each other's work. With investigative cases, you are likely to peer review one another's proposals, investigations, and persuasive materials. Recently, self-assessment has become a more frequent component of assessment in science, especially as more group work is done.

There are many ways to assess group products and group processes. Some instructors give a group grade and an individual grade. Other instructors include either peer evaluations or group self-evaluations in the grading process. If your instructor has not already explained how you will be assessed, you might want to discuss this.

(6) Why are cases a good way to learn biology?

An important goal of biology education is that you be able to apply what you learn in courses to your life. Scientific problem solving is a valuable tool in both professional and everyday life. It is important for you to do science as well as learn about it; and it is important for you to choose the problems to be studied and the resources you will use as you investigate the case.

By doing investigative cases, you engage in scientific inquiry. You will read critically, pose questions, analyze data, think critically, construct hypotheses, investigate options, interpret results, and communicate scientific arguments. No matter how your instructor chooses to use this book, investigative cases can be a useful and interesting tool in your study of biology.

Reprinted from Biological Inquiry: A workbook of *Investigative Cases*, Third Edition, by Jane B. Reece, et.al. (2011), Benjamin Cummings, a Pearson Education Company.

Box 15.1 Tips on preparing and using PowerPoint slides in a spoken presentation

Microsoft PowerPoint can be used to produce high-quality visual aids, assuming a computer and digital projector are available in the room where you intend to speak. The presentation is produced as a series of electronic 'slides' onto which you can insert images, diagrams and text. When creating your slides, bear the following points in mind:

- **Plan the structure of your presentation.** Decide on the main topic areas and sketch out your ideas on paper. Think about what material you will need (e.g. pictures, graphs) and what colours to use for background and text.
- **Choose slide layouts according to purpose.** Once PowerPoint is running, from the *Insert* menu select *New Slide > Choose an Autolayout*. You can then add material to each new slide to suit your requirements.
- **Select your background with care.** Many of the pre-set background templates available within the *Format* menu (*Apply design template* option) are best avoided, since they are over-used and fussy, diverting attention from the content of the slides. Conversely, flat, dull backgrounds may seem uninteresting, while brightly coloured backgrounds can be garish and distracting. Choose whether to present your text as a light-coloured font on a dark background (more restful but perhaps less engaging if the room is dark) or a dark-coloured font on a light background (more lively).
- **Use visual images throughout.** Remember the familiar maxim 'a picture is worth ten thousand words'. A presentation composed entirely of text-based slides will be uninteresting: adding images and diagrams will brighten up your talk considerably (use the *Insert* menu, *Picture* option). Images can be taken with a digital camera, scanned in from a printed version or copied and pasted from the Web, but you should take care not to break copyright regulations. 'Clipart' is copyright-free, but should be used sparingly as most people will have seen the images before and they are rarely wholly relevant. Diagrams can be made from components created using the *Drawing* toolbar while graphs and tables can be imported from other programs, e.g. Excel (Box 14.1 gives further specific practical advice on adding graphics, saving files, etc.).
- **Keep text to a minimum.** Aim for no more than 20 words on a single slide (e.g. four/five lines containing a few words per line). Use headings and sub-headings to structure your talk: write only

key words or phrases as 'prompts' to remind you to cover a particular point during your talk – never be tempted to type whole sentences as you will then be reduced to reading these from the screen during your presentation, which is boring.

- **Use a large, clear font style.** Use the *Slide Master* option within the *View* menu to set the default font to a non-serif style such as Arial, or Comic Sans MS, and an appropriate colour. Default fonts for headings and bullet points are intentionally large, for clarity. Do not reduce these to anything less than 28 point font size (preferably larger) to cram in more words: if you have too much material, create a new slide and divide up the information.
- **Animate your material.** The *Slide Show* menu provides a *Custom Animation* function that enables you to introduce the various elements within a slide, e.g. text can be made to *Appear* one line at a time, to prevent the audience from reading ahead and help maintain their attention.
- **Don't overdo the special effects.** PowerPoint has a wide range of features that allow complex slide transitions and animations, additional sounds, etc. but these quickly become irritating to an audience unless they have a specific purpose within your presentation.
- **Always edit your slides before use.** Check through your slides and cut out any unnecessary words, adjust the layout and animation. Remember the maxim 'less is more' – avoid too much text; too many bullet points; too many distracting visual effects or sounds.

When presenting your talk:

- **Work out the basic procedures beforehand.** Practise, to make sure that you know how to move forwards and backwards in your slideshow, turn the screen on and off, hide the mouse pointer, etc.
- **Don't forget to engage your audience.** Despite the technical gadgetry, *you* need to play an active role in the presentation, as explained elsewhere in this chapter.
- **Don't go too fast.** Sometimes, new users tend to deliver their material too quickly: try to speak at a normal pace and practise beforehand.
- **Consider whether to provide a handout.** PowerPoint has several options, including some that provide space for notes (e.g. Fig. 4.3). However, a handout should not be your default option, as there is a cost involved.

Reprinted from *Practical Skills in Biomolecular Sciences*, Third Edition, by Rob Reed, et.al. (2007), Pearson Education Limited, a Pearson Education Company.

Box 15.2 Hints on spoken presentations

In planning the delivery of your talk, bear the following aspects in mind:

- **Using notes.** Many accomplished speakers use abbreviated notes for guidance, rather than reading word-for-word from a prepared script. When writing your talk:
  - (a) **Consider preparing your first draft as a full script:** write in spoken English and keep the text simple, to avoid a formal, impersonal style. Your aim should be to *talk* to your audience, not to *read* to them.
  - (b) **If necessary, use note-cards with key words and phrases:** it is best to avoid using a full script in the final presentation. As you rehearse and your confidence improves, a set of note-cards may be an appropriate format. Mark the position of slides/key points, etc.: each note-card should contain details of structure as well as content. Your notes should be written/printed in text large enough to be read easily during the presentation (also check that the lecture room has a lectern light or you may have problems reading your notes if the lights are dimmed). Each note-card or sheet should be clearly numbered, so that you do not lose your place.
  - (c) **Decide on the layout of your talk:** give each sub-division a heading in your notes, so that your audience is made aware of the structure.
  - (d) **Memorise your introductory/closing remarks:** you may prefer to rely on a full written version for these sections, in case your memory fails, or if you suffer 'stage fright'.
  - (e) **Using PowerPoint** (Box 15.1): here, you can either use the 'notes' option (*View> Notes Page*), or you may even prefer to dispense with notes entirely, since the slides will help structure your talk, acting as an *aide-memoire* for your material.
- **Work on your timing.** It is essential that your talk is the right length and the correct pace:
  - (a) **Rehearse your presentation:** ask a friend to listen and to comment constructively on those parts that were difficult to follow, to improve your performance.
  - (b) **Use 'split times' to pace yourself:** following an initial run-through, add the times at which you

should arrive at the key points of your talk to your notes. These timing marks will help you keep to time during the final presentation.
  - (c) **Avoid looking at your wristwatch when speaking;** this sends a negative signal to the audience. Use a wall clock (where available), or take off your watch and put it beside your notes so that you can glance at it without distracting the audience.
- **Consider your image.** Make sure that the image you project is appropriate for the occasion:
  - (a) **Think about what to wear:** aim to be respectable without 'dressing up', otherwise your message may be diminished.
  - (b) **Maintain a good posture:** it will help your voice projection if you stand upright, rather than slouching, or leaning over a lectern.
  - (c) **Deliver your material with expression:** project your voice towards the audience at the back of the room and make sure you look round to make eye contact with all sections of the audience. Arm movements and subdued body language will help maintain the interest of your audience. However, you should avoid extreme gestures (it may work for some TV personalities but it is not recommended for the beginner).
  - (d) **Try to identify and control any repetitive mannerisms:** repeated 'empty' words/phrases, fidgeting with pens, keys, etc. will distract your audience. Note-cards held in your hand give you something to focus on, while laser pointers will show up any nervous hand tremors. Practising in front of a mirror may help.
- **Think about questions.** Once again, the best approach is to prepare beforehand:
  - (a) **Consider what questions are likely to come up, and prepare brief answers.** However, do not be afraid to say 'I don't know': your audience will appreciate honesty rather than vacillation if you don't have an answer for a particular question.
  - (b) **If no questions are asked, you might pose a question yourself** and then ask for opinions from the audience: if you use this approach, you should be prepared to comment briefly if your audience has no suggestions, to avoid the presentation ending in an embarrassing silence.

Appendix 1
Scientific Investigation

Introduction:

Biology is the study of the phenomena of life, and biological scientists—researchers, teachers, and students—observe living systems and organisms, ask questions, and propose explanations for those observations. Scientific investigation is a way of testing those explanations. Science assumes that biological systems are understandable and can be explained by fundamental rules or laws. Scientific investigations share some common elements and procedures, which are referred to as the *scientific method*. Not all scientists follow these procedures in a strict fashion, but each of the elements is usually present. Science is a creative human endeavor that involves asking questions, making observations, developing explanatory hypotheses, and testing those hypotheses. Scientists closely scrutinize investigations in their field, and each scientist must present his or her work at scientific meetings or in professional publications, providing evidence from observations and experiments that supports the scientist's explanations of biological phenomena.

In this lab topic, you will not only review the process that scientists use to ask and answer questions about the living world, but you will develop the skills to conduct and critique scientific investigations. Like scientists, you will work in research teams in this laboratory and others, collaborating as you ask questions and solve problems. Throughout this laboratory manual, you will be investigating biology using the methodology of scientists, asking questions, proposing explanations, designing experiments, predicting results, collecting and analyzing data, and interpreting your results in light of your hypotheses.

EXERCISE 1.1
Questions and Hypotheses

This exercise explores the nature of scientific questions and hypotheses. Before going to lab, read the explanatory paragraphs and then be prepared to present your ideas in the class discussion.

Lab Study A. Asking Questions

Scientists are characteristically curious and creative individuals whose curiosity is directed toward understanding the natural world. They use their study of previous research or personal observations of natural phenomena as a basis for asking questions about the underlying causes or reasons for these phenomena. For a question to be pursued by scientists, the phenomenon must be well defined and testable. The elements must be measurable and controllable.

There are limits to the ability of science to answer questions. Science is only one of many ways of knowing about the world in which we live. Consider, for example, this question: Do excessively high temperatures cause people to behave immorally? Can a scientist investigate this question? Temperature is certainly a well-defined, measurable, and controllable factor, but morality of behavior is not scientifically measurable. We probably could not even reach a consensus on the definition. Thus, there is no experiment that can be performed to test the question. Which of the following questions do you think can be answered scientifically?

1. Do kids who play violent video games commit more violence?
2. Did the consumption of seven cans of "energy drink" cause the heart attack of a motorcyclist in Australia?
3. Will increased levels of CO_2 in the atmosphere stimulate the growth of woody vines, such as poison ivy and kudzu?
4. How effective are extracts of marigold and rosemary as insect repellents?
5. Should it be illegal to sell organs, such as a kidney, for transplant purposes?

How did you decide which questions can be answered scientifically?

Lab Study B. Developing Hypotheses

As questions are asked, scientists attempt to answer them by proposing possible explanations. Those proposed explanations are called **hypotheses.** A hypothesis tentatively explains something observed. It proposes an answer to a question. Consider question 4, preceding. One hypothesis based on this question might be "Marigold and rosemary extracts are more effective than DEET in repelling insects." The hypothesis has suggested a possible explanation that compares the difference in efficacy between these plant extracts and DEET.

A scientifically useful hypothesis must be testable and falsifiable (able to be proved false). To satisfy the requirement that a hypothesis be falsifiable, it must be possible that the test results do not support the explanation. In our example, the experiment might be to spray one arm with plant extracts and the other with DEET. Then place both arms in a chamber with mosquitoes. If mosquitoes bite both arms with equal frequency or the DEET arm has fewer bites, then the hypothesis has been falsified. *Even though the hypothesis can be falsified, it can never be proved true.* The evidence from an investigation can only provide support for the hypothesis. In our example, if there are fewer bites on the arm with plant extracts than on the DEET-treated arm, then the hypothesis has not been proved, but has been supported by the evidence. Other explanations still must be excluded, and new evidence from additional experiments and observations might falsify this hypothesis at a later date. In science seldom does a single test provide results that clearly support or falsify a hypothesis. In most cases, the evidence serves to modify the hypothesis or the conditions of the experiment.

Science is a way of knowing about the natural world (Moore, 1993) that involves testing hypotheses or explanations. The scientific method can be applied to the unusual and the commonplace. You use the scientific method when you investigate why your once-white socks are now blue. Your hypothesis might be that your blue jeans and socks were washed together, an assertion that can be tested through observations and experimentation.

Students often think that controlled experiments are the only way to test a hypothesis. The test of a hypothesis may include experimentation, additional observations, or the synthesis of information from a variety of sources. Many scientific advances have relied on other procedures and information to test hypotheses. For example, James Watson and Francis Crick developed a model that was their hypothesis for the structure of DNA. Their model could only be supported if the accumulated data from a number of other scientists were consistent with the model. Actually, their first model (hypothesis) was falsified by the work of Rosalind Franklin. Their final model was tested and supported not only by the ongoing work of Franklin and Maurice Wilkins but also by research previously published by Erwin Chargaff and others. Watson and Crick won the Nobel Prize for their scientific work. They did not perform a controlled experiment in the laboratory but tested their powerful hypothesis through the use of existing evidence from other research. Methods other than experimentation are acceptable in testing hypotheses. Think about other areas of science that require comparative observations and the accumulation of data from a variety of sources, all of which must be consistent with and support hypotheses or else be inconsistent and falsify hypotheses.

The information in your biology textbook is often thought of as a collection of facts, well understood and correct. It is true that much of the knowledge of biology has been derived through scientific investigations, has been thoroughly tested, and is supported by strong evidence. However, scientific knowledge is always subject to novel experiments and new technology, any aspect of which may result in modification of our ideas and a better understanding of biological phenomena. The structure of the cell membrane is an example of the self-correcting nature of science. Each model of the membrane has been modified as new results have negated one explanation and provided support for an alternative explanation.

Application

Before scientific questions can be answered, they must first be converted to hypotheses, which can be tested. For each of the following questions, write an explanatory hypothesis. Recall that the hypothesis is a statement that explains the phenomenon you are interested in investigating.

1. Does supplemental feeding of birds at backyard feeders affect their reproductive success?
2. Do preschool boys in coed classes develop better verbal skills than boys in all-male classes?

Scientists often propose and reject a variety of hypotheses before they design a single test. Discuss with your class which of the following statements would be useful as scientific hypotheses and could be investigated using scientific procedures. Give the reason for each answer by stating whether it could possibly be falsified and what factors are measurable and controllable.

1. The use of pesticides in farming causes deformities in nearby frog populations.
2. Sea turtles are more likely to hatch during a new moon.
3. Drinking two or three cups of coffee a day reduces the risk of heart disease in women.
4. Manatees and elephants share a common ancestor.
5. Organic food is healthier than conventionally produced food.

EXERCISE 1.2

Designing Experiments to Test Hypotheses

The most creative aspect of science is designing a test of your hypothesis that will provide unambiguous evidence to falsify or support a particular explanation. Scientists often design, critique, and modify a variety of experiments and other tests before they commit the time and resources to perform a single experiment. In this exercise, you will follow the procedure for experimentally testing hypotheses, but it is important to remember that other methods, including observation and the synthesis of other sources of data, are acceptable in scientific investigations. An experiment involves defining variables, outlining a procedure, and determining controls to be used as the experiment is performed. Once the experiment is defined, the investigator predicts the outcome of the experiment based on the hypothesis.

Read the following description of a scientific investigation of the effects of sulfur dioxide on soybean reproduction. Then in Lab Study A you will determine the types of variables involved, and in Lab Study B, the experimental procedure for this experiment and for others.

INVESTIGATION OF THE EFFECT OF SULFUR DIOXIDE ON SOYBEAN REPRODUCTION

Agricultural scientists were concerned about the effect of air pollution, sulfur dioxide in particular, on soybean production in fields adjacent to coal-powered power plants. Based on initial investigations, they proposed that sulfur dioxide in high concentrations would reduce reproduction in soybeans. They designed an experiment to test this hypothesis (Figure 1.1). In this experiment, 48 soybean plants, just beginning to produce flowers, were divided into two groups, treatment and no treatment. The 24 treated plants were divided into four groups of 6. One group of 6 treated plants was placed in a fumigation chamber and exposed to 0.6 ppm (parts per million) of sulfur dioxide for 4 hours to simulate sulfur dioxide emissions from a power plant. The experiment was repeated on the remaining three treated groups. The no-treatment plants were divided similarly into four groups of 6. Each group in turn was placed in a second fumigation chamber and exposed to filtered air for 4 hours. Following the experiment, all plants were returned to the green-house. When the beans matured, the number of bean pods, the number of seeds per pod, and the weight of the pods were determined for each plant.

Lab Study A. Determining the Variables

Read the description of each category of variable; then identify the variable described in the preceding investigation. The variables in an experiment must be clearly defined and measurable. The investigator will identify and define *dependent, independent,* and *controlled variables* for a particular experiment.

The Dependent Variable

Within the experiment, one variable will be measured or counted or observed in response to the experimental conditions. This variable is the **dependent variable.** For the soybeans, several dependent variables are measured, all of which provide information about reproduction. What are they?

The Independent Variable

The scientist will choose one variable, or experimental condition, to manip-ulate. This variable is considered the most important variable by which to test the investigator's hypothesis and is called the **independent variable.** What was the independent variable in the investigation of the effect of sulfur dioxide on soybean reproduction?

Can you suggest other variables that the investigator might have changed that would have had an effect on the dependent variables?

Although other factors, such as light, temperature, time, and fertilizer, might affect the dependent variables, only one independent variable is usu-ally chosen. Why is it important to have only one independent variable?

Why is it acceptable to have more than one dependent variable?

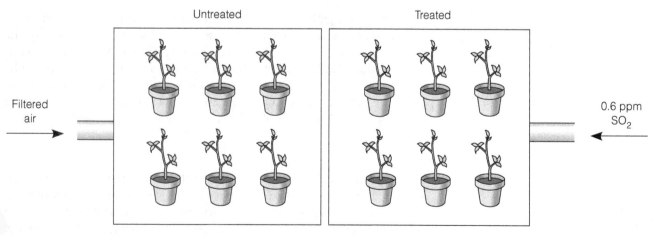

Figure A1.1.
Experimental design for soybean experiment. The experiment was repeated four times. Soybeans were fumigated for 4 hours.

The Controlled Variable

Consider the variables that you identified as alternative independent variables. Although they are not part of the hypothesis being tested in this investigation, they would have significant effects on the outcome of this experiment. These variables must, therefore, be kept constant during the course of the experiment. They are known as the **controlled variables.** The underlying assumption in experimental design is that the selected independent variable is the one affecting the dependent variable. This is only true if all other variables are controlled. What are the controlled variables in this experiment? What variables other than those you may have already listed can you now suggest?

Lab Study B. Choosing or Designing the Procedure

The **procedure** is the stepwise method, or sequence of steps, to be performed for the experiment. It should be recorded in a laboratory notebook before initiating the experiment, and any exceptions or modifications should be noted during the experiment. The procedures may be designed from research published in scientific journals, through collaboration with colleagues in the lab or other institutions, or by means of one's own novel and creative ideas. The process of outlining the procedure includes determining control treatment(s), levels of treatments, and numbers of replications.

Level of Treatment

The value set for the independent variable is called the **level of treatment.** For this experiment, the value was determined based on previous research and preliminary measurements of sulfur dioxide emissions. The scientists may select a range of concentrations from no sulfur dioxide to an extremely high concentration. The levels should be based on knowledge of the system and the biological significance of the treatment level. In some experiments however, independent variables represent categories that do not have a level of treatment (for example, gender). What was the level of treatment in the soybean experiment?

Replication

Scientific investigations are not valid if the conclusions drawn from them are based on one experiment with one or two individuals. Generally, the same procedure will be repeated several times (**replication**), providing consistent results. Notice that scientists do not expect exactly the same results inasmuch as individuals and their responses will vary. Results from replicated experiments are usually averaged and may be further analyzed using statistical tests. Describe replication in the soybean experiment.

Control

The experimental design includes a **control** in which the independent variable is held at an established level or is omitted. The control or control treatment serves as a benchmark that allows the scientist to decide whether the predicted effect is really due to the independent variable. In the case of the soybean experiment, what was the control treatment?

What is the difference between the control and the controlled variables discussed previously?

Lab Study C. Making Predictions

The investigator never begins an experiment without a prediction of its outcome. The **prediction** is always based on the particular experiment designed to test a specific hypothesis. Predictions are written in the form of if/then statements: "If the hypothesis is true, then the results of the experiment will be . . ."; for example, "**if** extracts of marigold and rosemary are more effective than DEET in repelling insects, **then** there will be fewer bites on the arm sprayed with the plant extract compared to the arm sprayed with DEET after a 5-minute exposure to mosquitoes." Making a prediction provides a critical analysis of the experimental design. If the predictions are not clear, the procedure can be modified before beginning the experiment. For the soybean experiment, the hypothesis was: "Exposure to sulfur dioxide reduces reproduction." What should the prediction be? State your prediction.

To evaluate the results of the experiment, the investigator always returns to the prediction. If the results match the prediction, then the hypothesis is supported. If the results do not match the prediction, then the hypothesis is falsified. Either way, the scientist has increased knowledge of the process being studied. Many times the falsification of a hypothesis can provide more information than confirmation, since the ideas and data must be critically evaluated in light of new information. In the soybean experiment, the scientist may learn that the prediction is true (sulfur dioxide does reduce reproduction at the concentration tested). As a next step, the scientist may now wish to identify the particular level at which the effect is first demonstrated.

Return to p. 4 and review your hypotheses for the numbered questions. Consider how you might design an experiment to test the first hypothesis. For example, you might count the number of eggs per nest or count the number of chicks successfully raised in a summer. The prediction might be:

> **If** supplemental feeding of birds at backyard feeders increases their reproductive success (*a restatement of the hypothesis*), **then** there will be more eggs per nest for birds with supplemental feeding compared to birds who receive no supplemental feeding (*predicting the results from the experiment*).

Now consider an experiment you might design to test the second hypothesis on p. 4. How will you measure "better verbal skills"?

State a prediction for this hypothesis and experiment. Use the if/then format.

The actual test of the prediction is one of the great moments in research. No matter the results, the scientist is not just following a procedure but truly testing a creative explanation derived from an interesting question.

Presenting and Analyzing Results:

Once the data are collected, they must be organized and summarized so that scientists can determine if the hypothesis has been supported or falsified. In this exercise, you will design **tables** and graphs; the latter are also called **figures.** Tables and figures have two primary functions. They are used (1) to help you analyze and interpret your results and (2) to enhance the clarity with which you present the work to a reader or viewer.

Lab Study A. Tables

You have collected data from your experiment in the form of a list of numbers that may appear at first glance to have little meaning. Look at your data. How could you organize the data set to make it easier to interpret? You could *average* the data set for each treatment, but even averages can be rather uninformative. Could you use a summary table to convey the data (in this case, averages)?

Table 1.4 is an example of a table using data averages of the number of seeds per pod and number of pods per plant as the dependent variables and exposure to sulfur dioxide as the independent variable. Note that the number of replicates and the units of measurement are provided in the table title.

Tables are used to present results that have a few too many data points. They are also useful for displaying several dependent variables and when the quantitative values rather than the trends are the focus. For example, average number of bean pods, average number of seeds per pod, and average weight of pods per plant for treated and untreated plants could all be presented in one table.

The following guidelines will help you construct a table.

- All values of the same kind should read down the column, not across a row. Include only data that are important in presenting the results and for further discussion.

- Information and results that are not essential (for example: test-tube number, simple calculations, or data with no differences) should be omitted.

- The headings of each column should include units of measurement, if appropriate.

- Tables are numbered consecutively throughout a lab report or scientific paper. For example: Table A1.1 would be the fourth table in your report.

- The **title,** which is located at the top of the table, should be clear and concise, with enough information to allow the table to be understandable apart from the text. Capitalize the first and important words in the title. Do not capitalize articles (a, an, the), short prepositions, and conjunctions. The title does not need a period at the end.

Table A1.1

Effects of 4-Hour Exposure to 0.6 ppm Sulfur Dioxide on Average Seed and Pod Production in Soybeans (24 Replicates)

Treatment	Seeds per Pod	Pods per Plant
Control	3.26	16
SO_2	1.96	13

- Refer to each table in the written text. Summarize the data and refer to the table; for example, "The plants treated with sulfur dioxide produced an average of 1.96 seeds per pod." Do not write."

- If you are using a database program, such as Excel, you should still sketch your table on paper before constructing it on the computer.

Lab Study B. Figures

Graphs, diagrams, drawings, and photographs are all called *figures*. The results of an experiment usually are presented graphically, showing the relationships among the independent and dependent variable(s). A graph or figure provides a visual summary of the results. Often, characteristics of the data are not apparent in a table but may become clear in a graph. By looking at a graph, then, you can visualize the effect that the independent variable has on the dependent variable and detect trends in your data. Making a graph may be one of the first steps in analyzing your results.

The presentation of your data in a graph will assist you in interpreting and communicating your results. In the final steps of a scientific investigation, you must be able to construct a logical argument based on your results that either supports or falsifies your starting hypothesis. Your graph should be accurately and clearly constructed, easily interpreted, and well annotated.

The following guidelines will help you to construct such a graph.

- Use graph paper and a ruler to plot the values accurately. If using a database program, you should first sketch your axes and data points before constructing the figure on the computer.

- The independent variable is graphed on the x axis (horizontal axis, or abscissa), and the dependent variable, on the y axis (vertical axis, or ordinate).

- The numerical range for each axis should be appropriate for the data being plotted. Generally, begin both axes of the graph at zero (the extreme left corner). Then choose your intervals and range to maximize the use of the graph space. Choose intervals that are logically spaced and therefore will allow easy interpretation of the graph, for example, intervals of 5s or 10s. To avoid generating graphs with wasted space, you may signify unused graph space by two perpendicular tic marks between the zero and your lowest number on one or both axes.

- Label the axes to indicate the variable and the units of measurement. Include a legend if colors or shading is used to indicate different aspects of the experiment.

- Choose the type of graph that best presents your data. Line graphs and bar graphs are most frequently used. The choice of graph type depends on the nature of the variable being graphed.

- Compose a title for your figure, and write it below your graph. Figures should be numbered consecutively throughout a lab report or scientific paper. Each figure is given a caption or title that describes its contents, giving enough information to allow the figure to be self-contained. Capitalize only the first word in a figure title and place a period at the end.

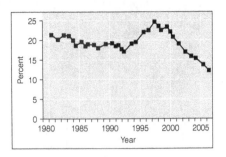

Figure A1.2.
Percent of 12th graders who smoked cigarettes daily. (*Forum on Child and Family Statistics*, 2009)

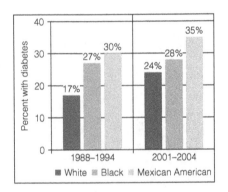

Figure A1.3.
Percent of people 65 or older in three racial groups with diabetes in the U.S. (*Centers for Disease Control*, 2008)

Reprinted from Investigating Biology Lab Manual, Seventh Edition, by Jane B. Reece, et.al. (2011), Benjamin Cummings, a Pearson Education Company.

The Line Graph

Line graphs show changes in the quantity of the chosen variable and emphasize the rise and fall of the values over their range. Use a line graph to present continuous quantitative data. For example, changes in the dependent variable, soybean weight, measured over time would be depicted best in a line graph.

- Plot data as separate points.
- Whether to connect the dots or draw a best fit curve depends on the type of data and how they were collected. To show trends, draw smooth curves or straight lines to fit the values plotted for any one data set. Connect the points dot to dot when emphasizing meaningful changes in values on the x axis.
- If more than one set of data is presented on a graph, use different colors or symbols and provide a key or legend to indicate which set is which.
- A boxed graph, instead of one with only two sides, makes it easier to see the values on the right side of the graph.

Note the features of a line graph in Figure A1.2, which shows the decline in smoking by high school seniors since 1998.

The Bar Graph

Bar graphs are constructed following the same principles as for line graphs, except that vertical bars, in a series, are drawn down to the horizontal axis. Bar graphs are often used for data that represent separate or discontinuous groups or nonnumerical categories, thus emphasizing the discrete differences between the groups. For example, a bar graph might be used to depict differences in number of seeds per pod for treated and untreated soybeans. Bar graphs are also used when the values on the x axis are numerical but grouped together. These graphs are called histograms.

Note the features of a bar graph in Figure A1.3, which shows the increase of diabetes in older citizens of three racial groups.

You will be asked to design graphs throughout this laboratory manual. Remember, the primary function of the figure is to present your results in the clearest manner to enhance the interpretation and presentation of your data.

Interpreting and Communicating Results:

The last component of a scientific investigation is to interpret the results and discuss their implications in light of the hypothesis and supporting literature. The investigator studies the results, including tables and figures and determines if the hypothesis has been supported or falsified. If the hypothesis has been falsified, the investigator must suggest alternate hypotheses for testing. If the hypothesis has been supported, the investigator suggests additional experiments to strengthen the hypothesis, using the same or alternate methods.

Scientists will thoroughly investigate a scientific question, testing hypotheses, collecting data, and analyzing results. In the early stages of a scientific study, scientists review the scientific literature relevant to their topic. They continue to review related published research as they interpret their results and develop conclusions. The final phase of a scientific investigation is the communication of the results to other scientists. Preliminary results may be presented within a laboratory research group and at scientific meetings where the findings can be discussed. Ultimately, the completed project is presented in the form of a scientific paper that is reviewed by scientists within the field and published in a scientific journal. The ideas, procedures, results, analyses, and conclusions of all scientific investigations are critically scrutinized by other scientists. Because of this, science is sometimes described as *self-correcting*, meaning that errors that may occur are usually discovered within the scientific community.

Scientific communication, whether spoken or written, is essential to science. During this laboratory course, you often will be asked to present and interpret your results at the end of the laboratory period. Additionally, you will write components of a scientific paper for many lab topics. In Appendix A at the end of the lab manual, you will find a full description of a scientific paper and instructions for writing each section.

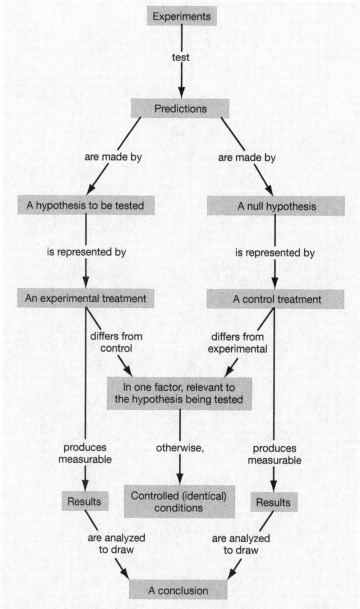

FIGURE A1.4   A Concept Map on Principles of Experimental Design.

Reprinted from *Biological Science*, Canadian Edition by Scott Freeman et al (2011), Pearson Education Canada.

Appendix 2
The Scientific Literature

Peer review refers to a process used by journals to prevent the publication of irrelevant experiments, unsupported interpretations, bad science and biased opinions. When an article is submitted to a peer reviewed journal, the editors locate peers (i.e., other scientists in a similar or related field) and have them critique the article based on a range of criteria, including the writing itself, the methodology used, the assumptions made, the validity of the hypothesis, the appropriateness of the experimental design, the relevance of the research to the field of study, the conclusions drawn and the interpretations made. Peer review may also be called *refereed* as the peers are expected to be neutral, have authority within the field, and their judgment is used to make a final 'call' or decision. These peers recommend whether or not an article is acceptable for publication. Depending on the areas of weakness identified, the author is given the opportunity to fix/address the problems and resubmit the article for further review.

A **Scholarly Article** is an article that is published in a peer-reviewed journal (also called a *scholarly journal*). These articles may be written by one person or by many people. A scholarly article is intended for a professional or academic reader and the language in which it is written tends to be formal and scientific (i.e., lots of hard to understand terminology!). Be aware that not all items in a scholarly journal are scholarly articles. A peer-reviewed journal will also publish opinions (also called editorials), news items, letters to the editor, and book reviews. Some of these other items might include a reference or two but a scholarly article ALWAYS includes a list of references.

Another type of publication that you might find is a **Magazine** and/or **Newspaper Article** (also called a *popular article* as they are written in a language that is easily understood by the majority of the population). Unless your assignment indicates you can use these as a source, they are best avoided as they are not peer-reviewed and are not original research.

Another set of terms that you need to be aware of are **Primary, Secondary, and Tertiary Sources**. These terms define a resource based on how close to the original research the information is. Thus, a **primary source** comes first and contains original research on which other research is based. This is usually the first formal appear of experimental results and MUST contain a results section and be written in the first person, e.g., "I (or we) conducted this experiment". A **secondary source** comes next and describes, interprets, analyses, evaluates, comments on, and discusses the content found in the primary source. In other words, the content of a secondary source repackages and reorganizes the already published information. The final

level is a **tertiary source**, which compiles, analyses and condenses secondary sources into a convenient, easy-to-read form (like a textbook).

Resources

This video defines and explains the peer review process from start to finish.
http://lib.ncsu.edu/tutorials/pr/

Citation and Citation Management

A **citation** is a reference to a specific work or portion of a work (e.g. a book chapter). A citation is composed of different pieces of information depending on what type of material is being cited. Therefore if you know how to read a citation and an item is cited correctly, you can tell immediately if you are looking for a journal, a book, a magazine, or a different source. To confuse things further, there are different citations styles. You have probably heard of some of them – MLA, APA, Chicago, ACS, CSE (to name a few acronyms). The most important thing to remember is that the style is just the way a journal or organization has decided they want the information in the citation to look – i.e. the order and formatting of the information, but MOST of the information you need should be there regardless of the style used. For this course you need to be familiar with the Citation Style used by the journal Nature. In the sections below, I have colour-coded examples (see colour-coded pdf on Blackboard course portal) of the most common items you will need to cite to help you identify the required information from each source.

Books

A citation to a book always includes publisher information. As journals, magazines and newspapers do not, books are relatively easy to identify.
A typical book citation looks like this:
Author. *Book Title*. (Publisher, Year).
Karl T. R., Melillo J. M., Peterson T. C. Global Climate Change Impacts in the United States (Cambridge University Press, 2009)
The one tricky thing about a book is that sometimes you will have a citation that refers to a particular chapter in a book. This means you will have more than one title – the book title and the chapter title BUT, unlike journals, magazines, and newspapers, you will still have the publisher information included at the end.
Here is an example of what I mean:
Debe, M. K. in Handbook of Fuel Cells—Fundamentals, Technology and Applications (eds Vielstich, W., Lamm, A. & Gasteiger, H. A.) Ch. 45 (John Wiley & Sons, 2003)
As you can see, there is a lot of extra information that was not in a 'typical' book citation.

Journal Articles

There are two key pieces to a journal article citation – one is that you have two titles (one for the article and one for the journal) and the other is that you will have a volume, sometimes an issue, and then page numbers for the article.
A typical journal citation looks like this:
Author. Article Title. *Journal Title*, *Volume*(Issue), Pages (Year)

Vörösmarty, C. J., Green, P., Salisbury, J. & Lammers, R. Global water resources: vulnerability from climate change and population growth. Science *289*, 284–288 (2000)

Webpage

References to websites should give authors if known, title of cited page, URL in full, and year of posting in parentheses.
A typical webpage citation looks like this:
Author. Page Title. *URL.* (Year)
Convention on Biological Diversity. Text of the Convention on Biological Diversity. *http://www.biodiv.org/convention/articles.asp.* (2004)

Resources

How to cite references in Nature Style:
http://www.nature.com/nature/authors/gta/index.html#a5.4

Sample Nature Paper: http://www.myaccess.library.utoronto.ca/login?url=http://simplelink.library.utoronto.ca/url.cfm/128294

Citation Management—Refworks

In class you will be (or have been) introduced to the citation management tool called Refworks. Here is a step by step guide to the key things you need to know/understand/do to make it work for you.

Step A. Set up an account

1. Go to Refworks—either via the Library Resources link in portal OR via the biology webpage of the UTM library **http://library.utm.utoronto.ca/subjects/science/biology**
2. Click on "Sign up for an Individual Account" and fill out the form to complete your registration.

Step B. Create a folder (or folders)

1. Click on Folders tab.
2. Create a new folder for your course.

Step C. Bring references into your folders

1. There are 2 steps to bringing your references into your folders, but which two steps they are depends on the database you choose to search.
2. Direct Download:
   a. In certain databases you can download citations directly into Refworks with the click of a button.
   b. Once they are imported into RefWorks you need to move them to your folder.
3. Indirect Download:
   a. In certain databases you must download your citations into a file.
   b. Once you have downloaded the file you can then import it into Refworks directly into the folder of your choice.

4. To determine which method you need to use, click on the pull down Help menu and choose Launch Help Menu

5. Within the Help Menu click on the Index. Type Data Vendors into the search box. This will pull up a list called "Importing from online data vendors", which gives instructions for importing from any database.

Step D. Get references out of your folders and into Microsoft Word (Mac and PC)

1. Click on the pull down Tools menu and choose Write-N-Cite.

2. Choose the version that you want and download the utility.

3. How utility displays depends on which version of Microsoft Word you have on your computer. If you have MS Vista or Word 2007 an icon will be visible in the Add-Ins tab. In earlier versions, an icon will be visible in the top menu.

4. When you are ready to cite a source, click on the icon, it will open up RefWorks. Choose the items you wish to cite and they will be placed in your document. The document will look odd as the computer will use it's own code. When you are finished, click on Bibliography and choose the format you want. Your document will be reformatted and your bibliography will be automatically generated.

Searching (and finding) the literature

Keywords are descriptive words used when you search for information on any topic. Typically, your results will include these words in the title, abstract, or subject heading/descriptor, depending on where you conduct your search. These words can be broad or narrow depending on the information that you are trying to find. A good way to come up with keywords is to use the same types of terms you would use when designing a concept map (see Appendix 1).

A **database** is a collection of data that has been systematically organized. The University of Toronto Library purchases access to databases that include citations to scholarly journal articles to help you find these articles more easily using keywords relating to your topic. The UTM library's biology webpage includes links to the most important databases for searching and finding biology papers – http://library.utm.utoronto.ca/subjects/science/biology

Appendix 3

A Quick Guide to Solving Genetics Problems

Name_____   Course/Section_____

Date_____   Professor/TA_____

 Activity 14.3 A Quick Guide to Solving Genetics Problems

Over the years, rules have been developed for setting up genetics problems and denoting genes and their alleles in these problems. This activity provides a quick review of some of these rules. After you have read through all of this material, complete Activities 14.4, 15.1, and 15.2.

Basic Assumptions to Make When Solving Genetics Problems

1. Are the genes linked?

If the problem does not (a) indicate that the genes are linked or (b) ask whether the genes are (or could be) linked, then you should assume that the genes are not linked.

2. Are the genes sex-linked?

Similarly, if the problem does not (a) indicate that the genes are sex-linked (that is, on the X chromosome) or (b) ask whether the genes are (or could be) on the X chromosome (or Y chromosome), then you should assume that the genes are on autosomes and are not sex-linked.

3. Is there a lethal allele?

If a gene is lethal, then you should assume that the offspring that get the lethal allele (if dominant) or alleles (if homozygous recessive) do not appear; that is, they are not born, do not hatch, and so on. Therefore, they are not counted among the offspring. An obvious exception is lethal genes that have their effect late in life. If this is the case, however, it should be noted in the question.

Reprinted from *Practicing Biology,* Fourth Edition, by Jane B. Reece, et.al. (2011), Benjamin Cummings, a Pearson Education Company.

4. Are the alleles dominant, recessive, or neither?

Unless the problem states otherwise, assume that capital letters (*BB*, for example) designate dominant alleles and lowercase letters (*bb*, for example) indicate recessive alleles. When there is codominance or incomplete dominance, the alleles are usually designated by the same capital letter and each one is given a superscript (for example, $C^R C^W$).

5. How are genotypes written?

Assume a gene for fur color in hamsters is located on the number 1 pair of homologous autosomes. Brown fur (*B*) is dominant over white fur (*b*). The genotype for fur color can be designated in different ways:

a. The alleles can be shown associated with the number 1 chromosome. In this notation, an individual heterozygous for this gene is designated as $|^B |^b$.

b. Most commonly, this notation is simplified to *Bb*.

In problems that involve sex-linked genes, the chromosomes are always indicated—for example, $X^A X^a$ and $X^a Y$.

6. What information do you need to gather before trying to solve a genetics problem?

Before trying to solve any problem, answer these questions:

a. What information is provided? For example:
   - What type of cross is it? Is it a monohybrid or dihybrid cross?
   - Are the genes sex-linked or autosomal?
   - Linked or unlinked?

b. What does the information provided tell you about the gene(s) in question? For example:
   - What phenotypes can result?
   - How many alleles does the gene have?
   - Are the alleles of the gene dominant? Recessive? Codominant?

c. Does the question supply any information about the individuals' genotypes? If so, what information is provided?
   - Grandparent information?
   - Parental (P) information?
   - Gamete possibilities?
   - Offspring possibilities?

Name_____   Course/Section_____

Solving Genetics Problems

1. What is a Punnett square?

Punnett squares are frequently used in solving genetics problems. A Punnett square is a device that allows you to determine all the possible paired combinations of two sets of characteristics. For example, if you wanted to determine all the possible combinations of red, blue, and green shirts with red, blue, and green pants, you could set up this Punnett square:

		Shirts		
		Red shirt	Blue shirt	Green shirt
Pants	Red pants			
	Blue pants			
	Green pants			

Similarly, if you wanted to determine the probability of a male (XY) and a female (XX) having a son or a daughter, you would first determine the possible gametes each could produce and then set up a Punnett square to look at all the possible combinations of male and female gametes. Here, meiosis dictates that the female's gametes get one of her X chromosomes or the other. In the male, the gametes get either the X chromosome or the Y. As a result, the Punnett square would look like this:

		Female's gamete possibilities	
		X	X
Male's gamete possibilities	X	XX	XX
	Y	XY	XY

2. **If you know the parents' genotypes, how can you determine what types of offspring they will produce?**

   a. **Autosomal genes:** For an autosomal gene that has the alleles *A* and *a*, the three possible genotypes are *AA*, *Aa*, and *aa*.

All possible combinations of matings and offspring for two individuals carrying the autosomal gene with alleles *A* and *a* are shown in the figure below.

If you know how to solve these six crosses you can solve any problem involving one or more autosomal genes.

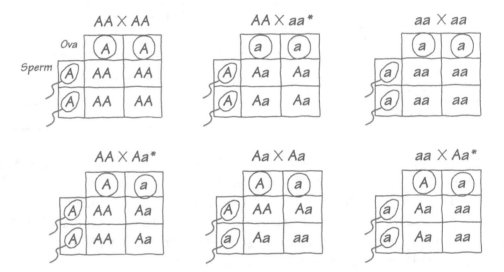

Note: If you take sex into account, there are actually nine possible combinations of matings:

	Female genotypes		
Male genotypes	*AA*	*Aa*	*aa*
AA	AA x AA	AA x Aa	**AA x aa**
Aa	Aa x AA	Aa x Aa	Aa x aa
aa	**AA x aa**	aa x Aa	aa x aa

Because the results of reciprocal autosomal matings—e.g., *AA* male with *aa* female and *aa* male with *AA* female—are the same, only one of each reciprocal type is included in the six combinations above.

Name_____   Course/Section_____

b. **Sex-linked genes:** For sex-linked genes that have two alleles, e.g., $w+$ and w, females have three possible genotypes: $X^{w+}X^{w+}$, $X^{w+}X^{w}$, and $X^{w}X^{w}$. Males have only two possible genotypes: $X^{w+}Y$ and $X^{w}Y$. All the possible combinations of matings and offspring for a sex-linked trait are listed in the next figure. If you know how to solve these six single-gene crosses, then you can solve any genetics problem involving sex-linked genes.

All possible combinations of matings for two individuals with a sex-linked gene are shown in the figure below. Fill in the Punnet squares to determine all possible combinations of offspring.

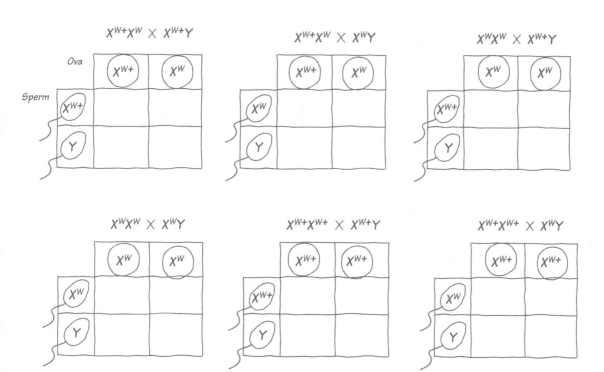

c. **Multiple genes:** Remember, if genes are on separate chromosomes, then they assort independently in meiosis. Therefore, to solve a genetics problem involving multiple genes, (where each gene is on a separate pair of homologous chromosomes):

- Solve for each gene separately.
- Determine probabilities for combination (multiple-gene) genotypes by multiplying the probabilities of the individual genotypes.

Example

What is the probability that two individuals of the genotype *AaBb* and *aaBb* will have any *aabb* offspring?

To answer this, solve for each gene separately.

A cross of *Aa* × *aa* could produce the following offspring:

	A	*a*
a	*Aa*	*aa*
a	*Aa*	*aa*

¹/₂ *Aa* and ¹/₂ *aa* offspring

A cross of *Bb* × *Bb* could produce the following offspring:

B	*BB*	*Bb*
b	*Bb*	*bb*
	B	*b*

¹/₄ *BB*, ¹/₂ *Bb*, and ¹/₄ *bb* offspring

The probability of having any *aabb* offspring is then the probability of having any *aa* offspring times the probability of having any *bb* offspring.

The probability is ¹/₂ × ¹/₄ = ¹/₈

A Quick Review of Hardy-Weinberg Population Genetics

Name_____   Course/Section_____

Date_____   Professor/TA_____

Activity 23.1 A Quick Review of Hardy-Weinberg Population Genetics

Part A. Complete the discussion by filling in the missing information.

If evolution can be defined as a change in gene (or more precisely, allele) frequencies, is it conversely true that a population not undergoing evolution should maintain a stable gene frequency from generation to generation? This was the question that Hardy and Weinberg answered independently.

1. **Definitions.** Complete these definitions or ideas that are central to understanding the Hardy-Weinberg theorem.

   a. Population: An interbreeding group of individuals of the same _____.
   b. Gene pool: All the alleles contained in the gametes of all the individuals in the

      _____.

   c. Genetic drift: Evolution (defined as a change in allele frequencies) that occurs in _____ populations as a result of chance events.

2. **The Hardy-Weinberg theorem.** The Hardy-Weinberg theorem states that in a population that _____ (**is/is not**) evolving, the allele frequencies and genotype frequencies remain constant from one generation to another.

3. **Assumptions.** The assumptions required for the theorem to be true are presented here in shortened form.

   a. The population is very _____.
   b. There is no net _____ of individuals into or out of the population.
   c. There is no net _____; that is, the forward and backward mutation rates for alleles are the same. For example, A goes to a as often as a goes to A.

d. Mating is at _____ for the trait/gene(s) in question.
e. There is no _____. Offspring from all possible matings for
    the trait/gene are equally likely to survive.

4. **The Hardy-Weinberg proof.** Consider a gene that has only two alleles,
    R (dominant) and r (recessive). The sum total of all R plus all r alleles equals all
    the alleles at this gene locus or 100% of all the alleles for that gene.

Let p = the percentage or probability of all the R alleles in the population
Let q = the percentage or probability of all the r alleles in the population

If all R + all r alleles = 100% of all the alleles, then

$$p + q = 1 \text{ (or } p = 1 - q \text{ or } q = 1 - p)$$

(*Note:* Frequencies are stated as percentages [for e.g., 50%] and their associated
probabilities are stated as decimal fractions [for e.g., 0.5].)

Assume that 50% of the alleles for fur color in a population of mice are B (black)
and 50% are b (brown). The fur color gene is autosomal.

a. What percentage of the gametes in the females (alone) carry the B allele? _____
b. What percentage of the gametes in the females (alone) carry the b allele? _____
c. What percentage of the gametes in the males carry the B allele? _____
d. What percentage of the gametes in the males carry the b allele? _____
e. Given the preceding case and all the Hardy-Weinberg assumptions, calculate the
    probabilities of the three possible genotypes (RR, Rr, and rr) occurring in all
    possible combinations of eggs and sperm for the population.

		Female gametes and probabilities	
		$\textcircled{R}(p)$	$\textcircled{r}(q)$
Male gametes and probabilities	$\textcircled{R}(p)$	$\underline{RR}\ (p^2)$	_____ ( )
	$\textcircled{r}(q)$	_____ ( )	_____ ( )

Because the offspring types represent all possible genotypes for this gene, it follows that

$$p^2 + 2pq + q^2 = 1 \text{ or } 100\% \text{ of all genotypes for this gene}$$

Name_____   Course/Section_____

Part B. Use your understanding of the Hardy-Weinberg theorem and proof to answer the questions.

1. According to the Hardy-Weinberg theorem, $p + q = 1$ and $p^2 + 2pq + q^2 = 1$. What does each of these formulas mean, and how are the formulas derived?

2. Assume a population is in Hardy-Weinberg equilibrium for a given genetic autosomal trait. What proportion of individuals in the population are heterozygous for the gene if the frequency of the recessive allele is 1%?

3. About one child in 2,500 is born with phenylketonuria (an inability to metabolize the amino acid phenylalanine). This is known to be a recessive autosomal trait.

    a. If the population is in Hardy-Weinberg equilibrium for this trait, what is the frequency of the phenylketonuria allele?

    b. What proportion of the population are carriers of the phenylketonuria allele (that is, what proportion are heterozygous)?

4. In purebred Holstein cattle, about 1 calf in 100 is spotted red rather than black. The trait is autosomal and red is recessive to black.

    a. What is the frequency of the red allele in the population?

    b. What is the frequency of black homozygous cattle in the population?

    c. What is the frequency of black heterozygous cattle in the population?

5. Assume that the probability of a sex-linked gene for color blindness is $0.09 = q$ and the probability of the normal allele is $0.91 = p$. This means that the probability of X chromosomes carrying the color blindness allele is 0.09 and the probability of X chromosomes carrying the normal allele is 0.91.

    a. What is the probability of having a color-blind male in the population?

    b. What is the probability of a color-blind female?

6. The ear tuft allele in chickens is autosomal and produces feathered skin projections near the ear on each side of the head. This gene is dominant and is lethal in the homozygous state. In other words, homozygous dominant embryos do not hatch from the egg. Assume that in a population of 6,000 chickens, 2,000 have no tufts and 4,000 have ear tufts. What are the frequencies of the normal versus ear tuft alleles in this population?

7. How can one determine whether or not a population is in Hardy-Weinberg equilibrium? What factors need to be considered?

8. Is it possible for a population's genotype frequencies to change from one generation to the next but for its gene (allele) frequencies to remain constant? Explain by providing an example.

Name_____   Course/Section_____

23.1 Test Your Understanding

In each of the following scenarios, state which assumption of the Hardy-Weinberg Law is being violated and give the basis for your choice.

1. In a particular region of the coast, limpets (a type of mollusc) live on near-shore habitats that are uniformly made up of brown sandstone rock. The principle predators of these limpets are shorebirds. The limpets occur in two morphs, one with a light-colored shell and one with a dark-colored shell. The shorebirds hunt by sight and are able to see the light limpets on the dark sandstone more easily than the dark limpets.

2. In *Chen caerulescens*, a species of goose, the white body form (the snow goose) and the blue body form (the blue goose) occasionally coexist. In these areas of contact, white-by-white and blue-by-blue matings are much more common than white-by-blue matings.

3. Prior to the Mongolian invasions that occurred between the 6th and 16th centuries, the frequency of blood type B across Europe was close to zero. The frequency of blood type B among the Mongols was relatively high. Today, it is possible to see fairly high frequencies of blood type B in the Eastern European countries and a gradual decrease in the frequency of blood type B as one moves from the Eastern European countries to the Western European countries such as France and England.

A Quick Guide to Genetics Problem Solving using Pedigree Analysis

(Written by Nikki Sarkar, UTM Biology Teaching Assistant)

This appendix is a quick guide to solving problems that require you to draw a pedigree based on a written family history and to calculated probabilities of genetic outcomes based on the given family history and the pedigree that you have drawn. What follows is a step-by-step approach to solving the problem(s) and addresses some of the common issues students encounter when attempting to solve these types of problems.

For some additional helpful information, see **Section 13.6** (Applying Mendel's Rules to Humans) and **BioSkills 9** (Combining Probabilities) of your text book, *Biological Science*.

Drawing the Pedigree and Assigning Genotypes

Sample Problem: The condition known as albinism is characterized by the lack of pigmentation of the skin, hair and eyes. Jim has discovered that this condition runs in his family. Based on the following information, draw the pedigree for Jim's family:
-His maternal uncle (i.e., the brother of his mother) has albinism.
-His maternal uncle has 4 children, none of whom have albinism.
-One of the sons of his maternal uncle has 2 daughters and 1 son. One of the daughters has albinism.
-The mother of his maternal grandfather has albinism.
-As far as Jim knows, no one on his father's side of the family has albinism.

Steps 1 and 2: **Draw the family tree and identify the affected individuals** (using the basic symbol conventions).

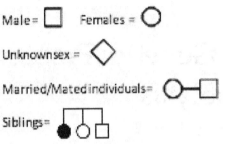

Male = ☐   Females = ○

Unknown sex = ◇

Married/Mated individuals = ○—☐

Siblings = ●○☐

Affected = shaded in symbol

*If dealing with 2 different traits, assign each half of the symbol to each trait...remember to include a legend identifying which trait is on which side...if this is really confusing, you can just draw 2 different pedigrees (1 for each trait)

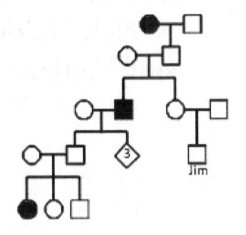

Step 3: **Determine mode of inheritance (for each trait being examined) based on the pattern of affected individuals.**

Some tell-tale patterns in determining mode of inheritance from pedigrees (this is NOT an exhaustive list):

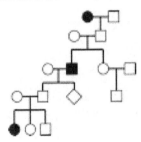

Autosomal Recessive: Affected individuals often seen in alternating generations (think about why); males and females are equally affected.

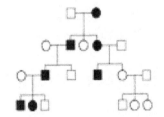

Autosomal Dominant: Affected individuals often seen in every generation (think about why); males and females are equally affected.

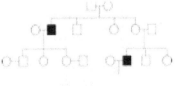

X-linked Recessive: Males more often affected; all sons of affected mothers are affected; all daughters of affected males are carriers.

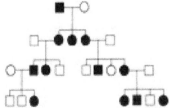

X-linked Dominant: Affected individuals seen in every generation; all daughters of affected males are affected; affected males have affected mothers.

Based on the pattern of affected individuals in Jim's family, albinism is likely an **autosomal recessive** trait.

Step 4: Assign genotypes based on the mode of inheritance.

Although the question or problem given may not explicitly say to assign the genotypes to the individuals in your pedigree, doing so will make identifying the carriers and answering some of the subsequent questions somewhat easier.

For our example, we have determined that albinism is an **autosomal recessive** trait so in order to exhibit the condition (or phenotype) the individual must be homozygous recessive (or "**aa**"). People carrying the trait (i.e., carrying one of the recessive alleles) are heterozygous ("**Aa**"). People not carrying the recessive allele are homozygous
dominant ("**AA**"). If we know that an individual is phenotypically normal but we are not sure if an individual is homozygous dominant or heterozygous, give the genotype as "**A-**".

When we start assigning genotypes, it is generally easiest to start with the individuals who are homozygous recessive (note that this is also true for 'dominant' traits; i.e., it is still easiest to identify the homozygous recessive individuals first).

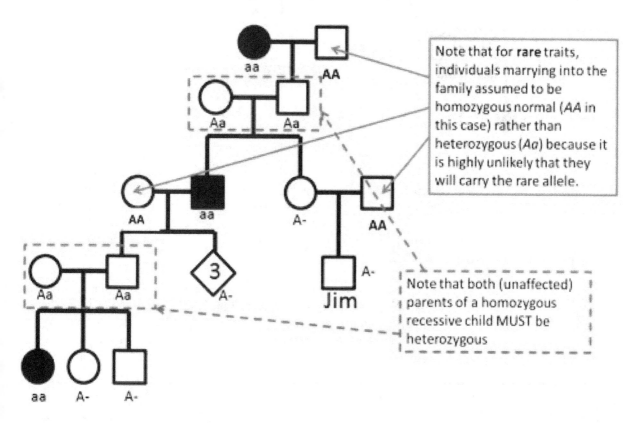

Note that for **rare** traits, individuals marrying into the family assumed to be homozygous normal (*AA* in this case) rather than heterozygous (*Aa*) because it is highly unlikely that they will carry the rare allele.

Note that both (unaffected) parents of a homozygous recessive child MUST be heterozygous

Note: If dealing with 2 different traits, make sure you use different letters when assigning the genotypes.

Note: If dealing with an X-linked trait, you can use the notation "$X^A X^A$" for homozygous dominant females, "$X^A X^a$" for heterozygous females, "$X^a X^a$" for homozygous recessive females, "$X^A Y$" for dominant males, and "$X^a Y$" for recessive males.

Determining the Probability of Specific Genetic Outcomes

Sample Problem (continued): Jim and his wife Jane are planning on having children. After discussions with Jane's family, they find out that the brother of her paternal grandfather had albinism. What is the probability that Jim and Jane will have a child with albinism?

Steps 1-4: We have already drawn the pedigree and determined the genotypes for the individuals in Jim's family, now we must do the same for Jane's family.

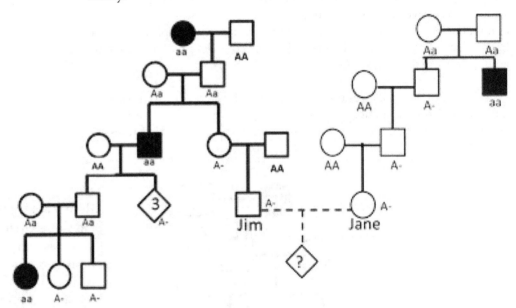

Step 5: After assigning genotypes to the members of Jim and Jane's families, we see that there is some possibility that both Jim and Jane carry the recessive albinism allele (i.e., that they are heterozygous). What is the probability that Jim carries the allele? What is the probability that Jane carries the allele?

The probability that Jim is "*Aa*" is equal to the probability that is father was "*Aa*" **AND** that he passed the "*a*" to Jim. Since both of these things have to happen for Jim to be a carrier, we use the **product rule** and multiply the probabilities together. The probability that Jim's father is "*Aa*" is ⅔.

*Note that in a situation involving a recessive trait where you know the parents are heterozygous (e.g. Aa x Aa), and you know the child is phenotypically normal, then the probability that the person is Aa is **2/3** (because you KNOW the child cannot be genotypically aa).

	A	**a**
A	AA	Aa
a	Aa	✗

If Jim's father is "*Aa*", the probability that he passes the "a" to Jim is ½. By multiplying these probabilities together, there is a ⅔ × ½ = ⅓ probability that Jim is heterozygous.

The probability that Jane is "*Aa*" is equal to the probability that her paternal grandfather is "*Aa*" **AND** that her grandfather passed the "*a*" to her father **AND** that her father passed the "*a*" to her. Since all of these things have to happen for Jane to be a carrier, we use the product rule and multiply the probabilities together. The probability that Jane's paternal grandfather is "*Aa*" is ⅔. If Jane's paternal grandfather is "*Aa*", the probability that he passed the "*a*" to Jane's father is ½. If Jane's father is "*Aa*", the probability that she passes the "*a*" to Jane is ½. Therefore, the probability that Jane is heterozygous is: ⅔ × ½ × ½ = ⅙.

Step 6: The probability that Jim and Jane will have an affected (homozygous recessive) child is equal to the probability that Jim is a carrier (⅓) **AND** passes the "*a*" to the child (½) **AND** that Jane is a carrier (⅙) **AND** passes the "*a*" to the child (½). Therefore, the probability that they will have an affected child is: ⅓ × ½ × ⅙ × ½ = 1/72.

Extensions

Sample Problem (continued): If Jim and Jane already have an affected child, what is the probability that their next child will also be affected? What is the probability that their next child will have **at least one co**py of the recessive allele?

If Jim and Jane already have an affected child, we know that they MUST both be heterozygous ("*Aa*"). **When determining the probability that their next child will be affected**, we no longer have to consider the complicated calculations used in Steps 5 and 6. Instead, we only have to consider the probability of producing a homozygous recessive offspring from an "*Aa* x *Aa*" cross—which is ¼.

The **probability that the next child will have at least one copy of the recessive allele** is equal to the probability that the child will be homozygous recessive (¼) **OR** that the child will be heterozygous (½). In this case we use the **sum rule** and add the two probabilities together: ¼ + ½ = ¾.

Appendix 6
Sterile Technique and Microbial Culture

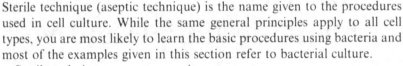

Sterile technique (aseptic technique) is the name given to the procedures used in cell culture. While the same general principles apply to all cell types, you are most likely to learn the basic procedures using bacteria and most of the examples given in this section refer to bacterial culture.

Sterile technique serves two main purposes:

1. To prevent accidental contamination of laboratory cultures due to microbes from external sources, e.g. skin, clothing or the surrounding environment.
2. To prevent microbial contamination of laboratory workers, in this instance you and your fellow students.

 KEY POINT All *microbial cell cultures should be treated as if they contained potentially harmful organisms. Sterile technique forms an important part of safety procedures, and must be followed whenever cell cultures are handled in the laboratory.*

Care is required because:

- You may accidentally isolate a harmful microbe as a contaminant when culturing a relatively harmless strain.
- Some individuals are more susceptible to infection and disease than others – not everyone exposed to a particular microbe will become ill.
- Laboratory culture involves purifying and growing large numbers of microbial cells – this represents a greater risk than small numbers of the original microbe.
- A microbe may change its characteristics, perhaps as a result of gene exchange or mutation.

The international biohazard symbol, shown in Figure 32.1, is used to indicate a significant risk due to a pathogenic microbe (p. 206).

Fig. 32.1 International symbol for a biohazard. Usually red on a yellow background, or black on a red background.

Sterilisation procedures

Given the ubiquity of microbes, the only way to achieve a sterile state is by their destruction or removal. Several methods can be used to achieve this objective:

Heat treatment

This is the most widespread form of sterilisation and is used in several basic laboratory procedures including the following:

- Red heat sterilisation. Achieved by heating metal inoculating loops, forceps, needles, etc., in a Bunsen flame (Fig. 32.2). This is a simple and effective form of sterilisation as no microbe will survive even a brief exposure to a naked flame. Flame sterilisation using alcohol is used for glass rods and spreaders (see below).
- Dry heat sterilisation. Here, a hot air oven is used at a temperature of at least 160 °C for at least 2 h. This method is used for the routine sterilisation of laboratory glassware. Dry heat procedures are of little value for items requiring repeated sterilisation during use.

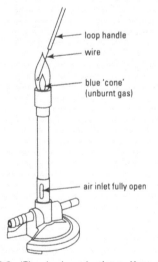

loop handle
wire
blue 'cone'
(unburnt gas)
air inlet fully open

Fig. 32.2 'Flaming' a wire loop. Keep the loop in the hottest part of the Bunsen flame (just outside the blue 'cone') until the wire is red hot.

Reprinted from *Practical Skills in Biomolecular Sciences*, Third Edition, by Rob Reed, et.al. (2007), Pearson Education Limited, a Pearson Education Company.

Fig. 32.3 Autoclave tape – the lower sample is untreated while the upper sample (with dark diagonal lines) has been autoclaved.

Using a sterile filter – most filters are supplied as pre-sterilised items. Make sure you follow a procedure that does not contaminate the filter on removal from its protective wrapping.

 SAFETY NOTE *When working with biocides, take care to avoid skin contact or ingestion, as most are toxic and irritant. If contact does occur, rinse with plenty of water.*

Using molten agar – a water bath (at 45–50°C) can be used to keep an agar-based medium in its molten state after autoclaving. Always dry the outside of the container on removal from the water bath, to reduce the risk of contamination from microbes in the water, e.g. during pour plating (p. 207).

- Moist heat sterilisation. This is the method of choice for many laboratory items, including most fluids, apart from heat-sensitive media. It is also used to decontaminate liquid media and glassware after use. The laboratory autoclave is used for these purposes. Typically, most items will be sterile after 15 min at 121 °C, although large items may require a longer period. The rapid killing action results from the latent heat of condensation of the pressurised steam, released on contact with cool materials in the autoclave. While special heat-sensitive tape (Fig. 32.3) is sometimes used to check that the autoclave is operating correctly, a better approach is to use spores of *Bacillus stearothermophilus*.

Radiation

Many disposable plastic items used in microbiology and cell biology are sterilised by exposure to UV or ionising radiation. They are supplied commercially in sterile packages, ready for use. Ultraviolet radiation has limited use in the laboratory, while ionising radiation (e.g. γ-rays) requires industrial facilities and cannot be operated on a laboratory scale.

Filtration

Heat-labile solutions (e.g. complex macromolecules, including proteins, antibiotics, serum) are particularly suited to this form of sterilisation. The filters come in a variety of shapes, sizes and materials, usually with a pore size of either 0.2 or 0.45 μm. The filtration apparatus and associated equipment are usually sterilised by autoclaving, or by dry heat. Passage of liquid through a sterile filter of pore size 0.2 μm into a sterile vessel is usually sufficient to remove bacteria but not viruses, so filtered liquids are not necessarily virus-free.

Chemical agents

These are known as disinfectants, or biocides, and are most often used for the disposal of contaminated items following laboratory use, e.g. glass slides and pipettes. They are also used to treat spillages. The term 'disinfection' implies destruction of disease-causing bacterial cells, although spores and viruses may not always be destroyed. Remember that disinfectants require time to exert their killing effect – any spillage should be covered with an appropriate disinfectant and left for at least 10 min before mopping up.

Use of laboratory equipment

Working area

One of the most important aspects of good sterile technique is to keep your working area as clean and tidy as possible. Start by clearing all items from your working surface, wipe the bench down with disinfectant and then arrange the items you need for a particular procedure so that they are close at hand, leaving a clear working space in the centre of your bench.

Media

Cells may be cultured in either a liquid medium (broth), or a solidified medium (p. 232). The gelling agent used in most solidified media is agar, a complex polysaccharide from red algae that produces a stiff transparent gel when used at 1–2% (w/v). Agar is used because it is relatively resistant to degradation by most bacteria and because of its rheological properties – an agar medium melts at 98 °C, remaining solid at all temperatures used for routine laboratory culture. However, once melted it does not solidify again until the temperature falls to about 44 °C. This means that heat-sensitive constituents (e.g. vitamins, blood, cells) can be added aseptically to the medium after autoclaving.

Inoculating loops

The initial isolation and subsequent transfer of microbes between containers can be achieved using a sterile inoculating loop. Most teaching laboratories use nichrome wire loops in a metal handle. A wire loop can be repeatedly sterilised by heating the wire, loop downwards and almost vertical, in the hottest part of a Bunsen flame until the whole wire becomes red hot (Fig. 32.2). Then the loop is removed from the flame to minimise heat transfer to the handle. After cooling for 8–10 s (without touching any other object) it is ready for use.

When resterilising a contaminated wire loop in a Bunsen flame after use, do not heat the loop too rapidly, as the sample may spatter, creating an aerosol: it is better to soak the loop for a few minutes in disinfectant than to risk heating a fully charged (contaminated) inoculating loop.

Containers

There is a risk of contamination whenever a sterile bottle, flask or test tube is opened. One method that reduces the chance of airborne contamination is quickly to pass the open mouth of the glass vessel through a flame. This destroys any microbes on the outer surfaces nearest to the mouth of the vessel. In addition, by heating the air within the neck of the vessel, an outwardly directed air flow is established, reducing the likelihood of microbial contamination.

It is general practice to flame the mouth of each vessel immediately after opening and then repeat the procedure just before replacing the top. Caps, lids and cotton wool plugs must not be placed on the bench during flaming and sampling: they should be removed and held using the smallest finger of one hand, to minimise the risk of contamination. This also leaves the remaining fingers free to carry out other manipulations. With practice, it is possible to remove the tops from two tubes, flame each tube and transfer material from one to the other while holding one top in each hand.

Laminar flow cabinets

These are designed to prevent airborne contamination, e.g. when preparing media or subculturing microbes or tissue cultures. Sterile air is produced by passage through a high efficiency particulate air (HEPA) filter: this is then directed over the working area, either horizontally (towards the operator) or downwards. The operator handles specimens, media, etc. through an opening at the front of the cabinet. Note that standard laminar flow cabinets do *not* protect the worker from contamination and must not be used with pathogenic microbes: special safety cabinets and laboratories are used for work with ACDP hazard group 3 and 4 microbes (Table 32.1) and for samples that might contain such pathogens.

Working with plastic disposable loops – *these are used in many research laboratories: pre-sterilised and suitable for single use, they avoid the hazards of naked flames and the risk of aerosol formation during heating. Discard into disinfectant solution after use.*

Using a Bunsen burner to reduce airborne contamination – *working close to the updraught created by a Bunsen flame reduces the likelihood of particles falling from the air into an open vessel.*

Using glass pipettes – *these are plugged with cotton wool at the top before being autoclaved inside a metal can. Flame the open end of the can on removal of a pipette, to prevent contamination of the remaining pipettes. Autopipettors and sterile disposable tips (p. 129) offer an alternative approach.*

Table 32.1 Classification of microbes on the basis of hazard. The following categories are recommended by the UK Advisory Committee on Dangerous Pathogens (ACDP)

Hazard group	Comments
1	Unlikely to cause human disease
2	May cause disease: possible hazard to laboratory workers, minimal hazard to community
3	May cause severe disease: may be a serious hazard to laboratory workers, may spread to community
4	Causes severe disease: is a serious hazard to laboratory workers, high risk to community

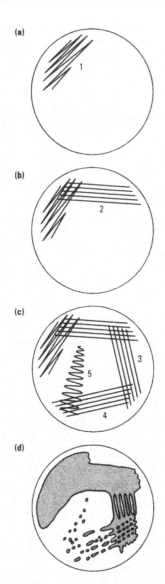

Fig. 32.4 Preparation of a streak plate for single colonies. (a) Using a sterile metal loop, take a small sample of the material to be streaked. Distribute the sample over a small sector of the plate (area 1), then flame the loop and allow to cool (approximately 8–10 s). (b) Make several small streaks from the initial sector into the adjacent sector (area 2), taking care not to allow the streaks to overlap. Flame the loop and allow to cool. (c) Repeat the procedure for areas 3 and 4, resterilising the loop between each step. Finally, make a single, long streak, as shown for area 5. (d) The expected result after incubation at the appropriate temperature (e.g. 37 °C for 24 h): each step should have diluted the inoculum, giving individual colonies within one or more sectors on the plate. Further subculture of an individual colony should give a pure (clonal) culture.

 KEY POINT *The most obvious risks when handling microbial cultures are those due to ingestion or entry via a cut in the skin – all cuts should be covered with a plaster or disposable plastic gloves. A less obvious source of hazard is the formation of aerosols of liquid droplets from microbial suspensions, with the risk of inhalation, or surface contamination of other objects.*

Microbiological hazards

The following steps will minimise the risk of aerosol formation:

- Use stoppered tubes when shaking, centrifuging or mixing microbial suspensions.
- Pour solutions gently, keeping the difference in height to a minimum.
- Discharge pipettes onto the side of the container.

Other general rules which apply in all laboratories include:

- Take care with sharp instruments, including needles and glass Pasteur pipettes.
- Do not pour waste cultures down the sink – they must be autoclaved.
- Put other contaminated items (e.g. slides, pipettes) into disinfectant after use.
- Wipe down your bench with disinfectant when practical work is complete.
- Always wash your hands before leaving the laboratory.

Plating methods

Many culture methods make use of a solidified medium within a Petri plate. A variety of techniques can be used to transfer and distribute the organisms prior to incubation. The three most important procedures are described below.

Streak dilution plate

Streaking a plate for single colonies is one of the most important basic skills in microbiology, since it is used in the initial isolation of a cell culture and in maintaining stock cultures, where a streak dilution plate with single colonies all of the same type confirms the purity of the strain. A sterile inoculating loop is used to streak the organisms over the surface of the medium, thereby diluting the sample (Fig. 32.4). The aim is to achieve single colonies at some point on the plate: ideally, such colonies are derived from single cells (e.g. in the case of unicellular bacteria, animal and plant cell lines) or from groups of cells of the same species (in filamentous or colonial forms). Single colonies, containing cells of a single species and derived from a single parental cell, form the basis of most pure culture methods (p. 211).

Note the following:

- Keep the lid of the Petri plate as close to the base as possible to reduce the risk of aerial contamination.
- Allow the loop to glide over the surface of the medium. Hold the handle at the balance point (near the centre) and use light, sweeping movements, as the agar surface is easily damaged and torn.
- Work quickly, but carefully. Do not breathe directly onto the exposed agar surface and replace the lid as soon as possible.

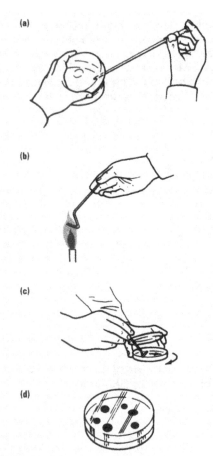

Fig. 32.5 Preparation of a spread plate. (a) Transfer a small volume of cell suspension (0.05–0.5 ml) to the surface of a solidified medium in a Petri plate. (b) Flame sterilise a glass spreader and allow to cool (8–10 s). (c) Distribute the liquid over the surface of the plate using the sterile spreader. Make sure of an even coverage by rotating the plate as you spread: allow the liquid to be absorbed into the agar medium. Incubate under suitable conditions. (d) After incubation, the microbial colonies should be distributed over the surface of the plate.

Spread plate

This method is used with cells in suspension, either in a liquid growth medium or in an appropriate sterile diluent. It is one method of quantifying the number of viable cells (or colony-forming units) in a sample, after appropriate dilution (p. 137).

An L-shaped glass spreader is sterilised by dipping the end of the spreader in a beaker containing a small amount of 70% v/v alcohol, allowing the excess to drain from the spreader and then igniting the remainder in a Bunsen flame. After cooling, the spreader is used to distribute a known volume of cell suspension across the plate (Fig. 32.5). *There is a significant fire risk associated with this technique*, so take care not to ignite the alcohol in the beaker, e.g. by returning an overheated glass rod to the beaker. The alcohol will burn with a pale blue flame that may be difficult to see, but will readily ignite other materials (e.g. a laboratory coat). Another source of risk comes from small droplets of flaming alcohol shed by an overloaded spreader onto the bench and this is why you *must* drain excess alcohol from the spreader *before* flaming. Some laboratories now provide plastic disposable spreaders for student use, to avoid the risk of fire.

Pour plate

This procedure also uses cells in suspension, but requires molten agar medium, usually in screw-capped bottles containing sufficient medium to prepare a single Petri plate (i.e. 15–20 ml), maintained in a water bath at 45–50 °C. A known volume of cell suspension is mixed with this molten agar, distributing the cells throughout the medium. This is then poured without delay into an empty sterile Petri plate and incubated, giving widely spaced colonies (Fig. 32.6). Furthermore, as most of the colonies are formed within the medium, they are far smaller than those of the surface streak method, allowing higher cell numbers to be counted (e.g. over 100 colonies per plate): some workers pour a thin layer of molten agar onto the surface of a pour plate after it has set, to ensure that no surface colonies are produced. Most bacteria and fungi are not killed by brief exposure to temperatures of 45–50 °C, though the procedure may be more damaging to microbes from low temperature conditions, e.g. psychrophilic bacteria.

One disadvantage of the pour plate method is that the typical colony morphology seen in surface-grown cultures will not be observed for those colonies that develop within the agar medium. A further disadvantage is that some of the suspension will be left behind in the screw-capped bottle. This can be avoided by transferring the suspension to the Petri plate, adding the molten agar, then swirling the plate to mix the two liquids. However, even when the plate is swirled repeatedly and in several directions, the liquids are not mixed as evenly as in the former procedure.

 KEY POINT *When working with molten agar, keep tubes and bottles of molten agar in a water bath until you are ready to use them, as they will begin to set within a couple of minutes at room temperature.*

QR Codes List

Throughout this text, you will notice a series of barcodes known as "QR Codes." Scanning these codes using a special QR application on your smart phone or other device will connect you to a website that will provide additional information about the topics in this text. The following is a list of the URLs that correspond to each of the QR codes, and the pages on which they are located:

Page number/Location on page	Link
14	http://www.utm.utoronto.ca/~w3reisz/
20 Top code	http://learn.genetics.utah.edu/units/biotech/extraction/
20 Middle code	http://www.youtube.com/watch?v=p3OzDndzcxs
20 Bottom code	http://www.youtube.com/watch?v=iyb7fwduuGM
21	http://utm.utoronto.ca/biology/people/short-steven-m
43	http://www.utm.utoronto.ca/~bstewart/
51	http://erin.utoronto.ca/~kohnmank/index.htm
58	http://learn.genetics.utah.edu/CONTENT/BEGIN/TRAITS/PTC/
59	http://utm.utoronto.ca/biology/people/levine-joel
68	http://health.howstuffworks.com/question692.htm
69	http://utm.utoronto.ca/BIOLOGY/PEOPLE/ESPIE-GEORGE
78	http://labs.eeb.utoronto.ca/gwynne/
100	http://lib.ncsu.edu/tutorials/pr/
101 Top code	http://www.nature.com/nature/authors/gta/index.html#a5.4
101 Middle code	http://www.myaccess.library.utoronto.ca/login?url=http://simplelink.library.utoronto.ca/url.cfm/128294
101 Bottom code	http://library.utm.utoronto.ca/subjects/science/biology
102	http://library.utm.utoronto.ca/subjects/science/biology